Mathematics **Level E**

PEOPLES

Common Core

Seeds for Success!

From the publisher of **Measuring Up**

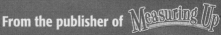

peopleseducation.com

Peoples Education
Your partner in student success

Executive Vice President, Chief Creative Officer: Diane Miller

Editorial Development: Publisher's Partnership

Managing Editor: Kerri Gero

Editorial Assistant: Amy Priddy Wierzbicki

Copy Editor: Katy Leclercq

Vice President of Marketing: Victoria Ameer Kiely

Senior Marketing Manager: Christine Grasso

Marketing Manager: Victoria Leo

Production Director: Jason Grasso

Production Manager: Jennifer Bridges Brewer

Assistant Production Managers: Steven Genzano, Jennifer Tully

Director of Permissions: Kristine Liebman

Cover Design: Joe Guerrero, Todd Kochakji

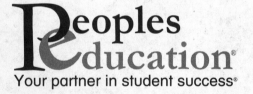

Your partner in student success®

Copyright © 2011
Peoples Education, Inc.
299 Market Street
Saddle Brook, New Jersey 07663

ISBN 978-1-61734-667-5

Printed in the United States of America.

Manufactured in Massachusetts in October 2010 by Bradford & Bigelow.

10   9   8   7   6   5   4   3   2   1

Table of Contents

Your teacher may choose to assign the pretest to diagnose your CCSS proficiency and direct you to help in this worktext.

CHAPTER 1 Chapter 1: Operations & Algebraic Thinking

CHAPTER 2 Numbers and Operations in Base 10

CHAPTER 3 Numbers & Operations-Fractions

CHAPTER 4 Measurement & Data

CHAPTER 5 Geometry

Your teacher may choose to assign the posttest for this program to check your learning.

Practice Path
Check out our Common Core web-based programs for access to thousands of additional practice items.

Grade 5 Common Core State Standards Overview

Operations and Algebraic Thinking
- Write and interpret numerical expressions.

- Analyze patterns and relationships.

Number and Operations in Base Ten
- Understand the place value system.

- Perform operations with multi-digit whole numbers and with decimals to hundredths.

Number and Operations—Fractions
- Use equivalent fractions as a strategy to add and subtract fractions.

- Apply and extend previous understandings of multiplication and division to multiply and divide fractions.

Measurement and Data
- Convert like measurement units within a given measurement system.

- Represent and interpret data.

- Geometric measurement: understand concepts of volume and relate volume to multiplication and to addition.

Geometry
- Graph points on the coordinate plane to solve real-world and mathematical problems.

- Classify two-dimensional figures into categories based on their properties.

Mathematical Practices
1. Make sense of problems and persevere in solving them.
2. Reason abstractly and quantitatively.
3. Construct viable arguments and critique the reasoning of others.
4. Model with mathematics.
5. Use appropriate tools strategically.
6. Attend to precision.
7. Look for and make use of structure.
8. Look for and express regularity in repeated reasoning.

Correlation to the Common Core State Standards

This worktext is customized to the Common Core State Standards for Mathematics. Most lessons focus on one content standard for in-depth review. Mathematical Practices are interwoven throughout each lesson to connect practices to content at point-of-use and promote depth of understanding.

Common Core State Standards	Lessons
Mathematical Practices	
1. Make sense of problems and persevere in solving them.	embedded throughout
2. Reason abstractly and quantitatively.	embedded throughout
3. Construct viable arguments and critique the reasoning of others.	embedded throughout
4. Model with mathematics.	embedded throughout
5. Use appropriate tools strategically.	embedded throughout
6. Attend to precision.	embedded throughout
7. Look for and make use of structure.	embedded throughout
8. Look for and express regularity in repeated reasoning.	embedded throughout
5.OA Operations and Algebraic Thinking	
Write and interpret numerical expressions.	
1. Use parentheses, brackets, or braces in numerical expressions, and evaluate expressions with these symbols.	1
2. Write simple expressions that record calculations with numbers, and interpret numerical expressions without evaluating them. *For example, express the calculation "add 8 and 7, then multiply by 2" as 2 × (8 + 7). Recognize that 3 × (18932 + 921) is three times as large as 18932 + 921, without having to calculate the indicated sum or product.*	2, 3
Analyze patterns and relationships.	
3. Generate two numerical patterns using two given rules. Identify apparent relationships between corresponding terms. Form ordered pairs consisting of corresponding terms from the two patterns, and graph the ordered pairs on a coordinate plane. *For example, given the rule "Add 3" and the starting number 0, and given the rule "Add 6" and the starting number 0, generate terms in the resulting sequences, and observe that the terms in one sequence are twice the corresponding terms in the other sequence. Explain informally why this is so.*	4, 5
5.NBT Number and Operations in Base Ten	
Understand the place value system.	
1. Recognize that in a multi-digit number, a digit in one place represents 10 times as much as it represents in the place to its right and $\frac{1}{10}$ of what it represents in the place to its left.	6

Common Core State Standards	Lessons
2. Explain patterns in the number of zeros of the product when multiplying a number by powers of 10, and explain patterns in the placement of the decimal point when a decimal is multiplied or divided by a power of 10. Use whole-number exponents to denote powers of 10.	7, 8, 9
3. Read, write, and compare decimals to thousandths.	10, 11
a. Read and write decimals to thousandths using base-ten numerals, number names, and expanded form, e.g., $347.392 = 3 \times 100 + 4 \times 10 + 7 \times 1 + 3 \times (1/10) + 9 \times (1/100) + 2 \times (1/1000)$.	10
b. Compare two decimals to thousandths based on meanings of the digits in each place, using >, =, and < symbols to record the results of comparisons.	11
4. Use place value understanding to round decimals to any place.	12
Perform operations with multi-digit whole numbers and with decimals to hundredths.	
5. Fluently multiply multi-digit whole numbers using the standard algorithm.	13
6. Find whole-number quotients of whole numbers with up to four-digit dividends and two-digit divisors, using strategies based on place value, the properties of operations, and/or the relationship between multiplication and division. Illustrate and explain the calculation by using equations, rectangular arrays, and/or area models.	14, 15, 16
7. Add, subtract, multiply, and divide decimals to hundredths, using concrete models or drawings and strategies based on place value, properties of operations, and/or the relationship between addition and subtraction; relate the strategy to a written method and explain the reasoning used.	17, 18
5.NF Number and Operations-Fractions	
Use equivalent fractions as a strategy to add and subtract fractions.	
1. Add and subtract fractions with unlike denominators (including mixed numbers) by replacing given fractions with equivalent fractions in such a way as to produce an equivalent sum or difference of fractions with like denominators. *For example, $\frac{2}{3} + \frac{5}{4} = \frac{8}{12} + \frac{15}{12} = \frac{23}{12}$. (In general, $\frac{a}{b} + \frac{c}{d} = \frac{(ad + bc)}{bd}$.)*	19
2. Solve word problems involving addition and subtraction of fractions referring to the same whole, including cases of unlike denominators, e.g., by using visual fraction models or equations to represent the problem. Use benchmark fractions and number sense of fractions to estimate mentally and assess the reasonableness of answers. *For example, recognize an incorrect result 2/5 + 1/2 = 3/7, by observing that 3/7 < 1/2.*	20
Apply and extend previous understandings of multiplication and division to multiply and divide fractions.	
3. Interpret a fraction as division of the numerator by the denominator ($\frac{a}{b} = a \div b$). Solve word problems involving division of whole numbers leading to answers in the form of fractions or mixed numbers, e.g., by using visual fraction models or equations to represent the problem. *For example, interpret $\frac{3}{4}$ as the result of dividing 3 by 4, noting that $\frac{3}{4}$ multiplied by 4 equals 3, and that when 3 wholes are shared equally among 4 people each person has a share of size $\frac{3}{4}$. If 9 people want to share a 50-pound sack of rice equally by weight, how many pounds of rice should each person get? Between what two whole numbers does your answer lie?*	21, 22
4. Apply and extend previous understandings of multiplication to multiply a fraction or whole number by a fraction.	23, 24
a. Interpret the product $(\frac{a}{b}) \times q$ as a parts of a partition of q into b equal parts; equivalently, as the result of a sequence of operations $a \times q \div b$. *For example, use a visual fraction model to show $(\frac{2}{3}) \times 4 = \frac{8}{3}$, and create a story context for this equation. Do the same with $(\frac{2}{3}) \times (\frac{4}{5}) = \frac{8}{15}$. (In general, $(\frac{a}{b}) \times (\frac{c}{d}) = \frac{ac}{bd}$.)*	23

Common Core State Standards	Lessons
b. Find the area of a rectangle with fractional side lengths by tiling it with unit squares of the appropriate unit fraction side lengths, and show that the area is the same as would be found by multiplying the side lengths. Multiply fractional side lengths to find areas of rectangles, and represent fraction products as rectangular areas.	24
5. Interpret multiplication as scaling (resizing), by:	25, 26
a. Comparing the size of a product to the size of one factor on the basis of the size of the other factor, without performing the indicated multiplication.	25
b. Explaining why multiplying a given number by a fraction greater than 1 results in a product greater than the given number (recognizing multiplication by whole numbers greater than 1 as a familiar case); explaining why multiplying a given number by a fraction less than 1 results in a product smaller than the given number; and relating the principle of fraction equivalence $\frac{a}{b} = \frac{(n \times a)}{(n \times b)}$ to the effect of multiplying $\frac{a}{b}$ by 1.	26
6. Solve real world problems involving multiplication of fractions and mixed numbers, e.g., by using visual fraction models or equations to represent the problem.	27
7. Apply and extend previous understandings of division to divide unit fractions by whole numbers and whole numbers by unit fractions.	28, 29, 30
a. Interpret division of a unit fraction by a non-zero whole number, and compute such quotients. *For example, create a story context for $(\frac{1}{3}) \div 4$, and use a visual fraction model to show the quotient. Use the relationship between multiplication and division to explain that $(\frac{1}{3}) \div 4 = \frac{1}{12}$ because $(\frac{1}{12}) \times 4 = \frac{1}{3}$.*	28
b. Interpret division of a whole number by a unit fraction, and compute such quotients. *For example, create a story context for $4 \div (\frac{1}{5})$, and use a visual fraction model to show the quotient. Use the relationship between multiplication and division to explain that $4 \div (\frac{1}{5}) = 20$ because $20 \times (\frac{1}{5}) = 4$.*	29
c. Solve real world problems involving division of unit fractions by non-zero whole numbers and division of whole numbers by unit fractions, e.g., by using visual fraction models and equations to represent the problem. *For example, how much chocolate will each person get if 3 people share $\frac{1}{2}$ lb of chocolate equally? How many $\frac{1}{3}$-cup servings are in 2 cups of raisins?*	30
5.MD Measurement and Data	
Convert like measurement units within a given measurement system.	
1. Convert among different-sized standard measurement units within a given measurement system (e.g., convert 5 cm to 0.05 m), and use these conversions in solving multi-step, real world problems.	31
Represent and interpret data.	
2. Make a line plot to display a data set of measurements in fractions of a unit ($\frac{1}{2}, \frac{1}{4}, \frac{1}{8}$). Use operations on fractions for this grade to solve problems involving information presented in line plots. *For example, given different measurements of liquid in identical beakers, find the amount of liquid each beaker would contain if the total amount in all the beakers were redistributed equally.*	32
Geometric measurement: understand concepts of volume and relate volume to multiplication and to addition.	
3. Recognize volume as an attribute of solid figures and understand concepts of volume measurement.	33, 34
a. A cube with side length 1 unit, called a "unit cube," is said to have "one cubic unit" of volume, and can be used to measure volume.	33

Common Core State Standards	Lessons
b. A solid figure which can be packed without gaps or overlaps using n unit cubes is said to have a volume of n cubic units.	34
4. Measure volumes by counting unit cubes, using cubic cm, cubic in, cubic ft, and improvised units.	35
5. Relate volume to the operations of multiplication and addition and solve real world and mathematical problems involving volume.	36, 37, 38
a. Find the volume of a right rectangular prism with whole-number side lengths by packing it with unit cubes, and show that the volume is the same as would be found by multiplying the edge lengths, equivalently by multiplying the height by the area of the base. Represent threefold whole-number products as volumes, e.g., to represent the associative property of multiplication.	36
b. Apply the formulas $V = l \times w \times h$ and $V = b \times h$ for rectangular prisms to find volumes of right rectangular prisms with whole-number edge lengths in the context of solving real world and mathematical problems.	37
c. Recognize volume as additive. Find volumes of solid figures composed of two non-overlapping right rectangular prisms by adding the volumes of the non-overlapping parts, applying this technique to solve real world problems.	38
5.G Geometry	
Graph points on the coordinate plane to solve real-world and mathematical problems.	
1. Use a pair of perpendicular number lines, called axes, to define a coordinate system, with the intersection of the lines (the origin) arranged to coincide with the 0 on each line and a given point in the plane located by using an ordered pair of numbers, called its coordinates. Understand that the first number indicates how far to travel from the origin in the direction of one axis, and the second number indicates how far to travel in the direction of the second axis, with the convention that the names of the two axes and the coordinates correspond (e.g., x-axis and x-coordinate, y-axis and y-coordinate).	39
2. Represent real world and mathematical problems by graphing points in the first quadrant of the coordinate plane, and interpret coordinate values of points in the context of the situation.	40
Classify two-dimensional figures into categories based on their properties.	
3. Understand that attributes belonging to a category of two-dimensional figures also belong to all subcategories of that category. *For example, all rectangles have four right angles and squares are rectangles, so all squares have four right angles.*	41
4. Classify two-dimensional figures in a hierarchy based on properties.	42

To the Student:

It's never too soon to prepare for your future. The same goes for learning the new Common Core State Standards for your grade level. This new set of expectations will help you be prepared for college and your career, and to be successful in all your academic pursuits.

The lessons in this book are geared toward helping you master all the Common Core State Standards for mathematics in a structured way.

Peoples Common Core has 5 chapters, each one is focused on a different set of skills and modeled on the Common Core State Standards.

Each chapter includes:

- A brief review of skills and key vocabulary

- Suggested tools to help you learn

- Real world examples

- Step-by-step problem-solving instruction

- A variety of activities and questions that allow you to show your learning

- Multiple-choice, short-answer, and extended-response question practice

- A special Kick It Up project and activity to boost your learning to the next level

These lessons will help you build your mathematics skills and improve your high-level thinking. The lessons may seem challenging at first, but keep at it and you will be a success!

Have a great school year!

Common Core

To Parents and Families:

Peoples Education has created this Common Core book to help your child master the new Common Core State Standards, and to get your child to think on a higher level. The Common Core State Standards are a clear set of K–12 grade-specific expectations. Developed by a consortium of states and coordinated by the National Governors Association and the Council of Chief State School Officers, these standards define what it means for students to be college- and career-ready in the 21st century. As your child moves through this book, encourage your child to consider, analyze, interpret, and evaluate instead of just recalling simple facts.

Each of the 5 chapters in this book is focused on a different set of skills, modeled on the Common Core State Standards.

Each chapter includes:

- A review of skills and key vocabulary

- Real world examples

- Step-by-step problem-solving instruction

- A variety of activities and questions that allow your child to show his or her skill comprehension

- Multiple-choice, short-answer, and extended-response question practice, as well as writing prompts

- A special Kick It Up project and activity to boost your child's learning to the next level

For success in school and the real world, your child needs a solid mathematics foundation, and your involvement is crucial to that success. Here are some suggestions:

Show that mathematics is important, by including your child in activities that require mathematical thinking.

Help find appropriate Internet sites for mathematics. Note how mathematics is used when you are out with your family. Discuss how mathematics is used in financial and banking matters, in careers such as engineering, architecture, and medicine, in space exploration, and in other real-life situations.

Encourage your child to take time to review and check his or her homework. Just solving a problem is not enough. Ask your child whether the answer is reasonable and have him or her explain what led to that answer.

Get involved! Work with us this year to ensure your child's success. Mathematics skills are an essential part of college and career readiness and the real world.

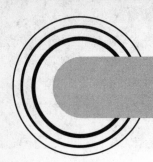

What's Inside

Lessons in this worktext provide instruction, activities, and review for each skill in the Common Core State Standards.

Real World Connections helps you understand the skill with examples and problems from real life. Toolbox lists supplies needed for the lesson, and Key Words highlight the words you will need to know.

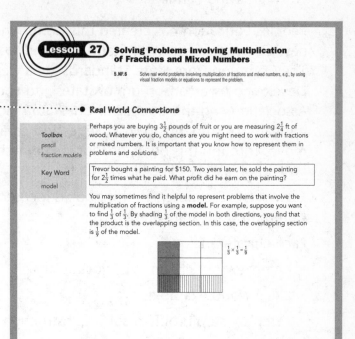

Lesson **27** Solving Problems Involving Multiplication of Fractions and Mixed Numbers

5.NF.6 Solve real world problems involving multiplication of fractions and mixed numbers, e.g., by using visual fraction models or equations to represent the problem.

● Real World Connections

Toolbox
pencil
fraction models

Key Word
model

Perhaps you are buying $3\frac{1}{2}$ pounds of fruit or you are measuring $2\frac{1}{4}$ ft of wood. Whatever you do, chances are you might need to work with fractions or mixed numbers. It is important that you know how to represent them in problems and solutions.

Trevor bought a painting for $150. Two years later, he sold the painting for $2\frac{1}{2}$ times what he paid. What profit did he earn on the painting?

You may sometimes find it helpful to represent problems that involve the multiplication of fractions using a **model.** For example, suppose you want to find $\frac{1}{3}$ of $\frac{1}{3}$. By shading $\frac{1}{3}$ of the model in both directions, you find that the product is the overlapping section. In this case, the overlapping section is $\frac{1}{9}$ of the model.

$$\frac{1}{3} \times \frac{1}{3} = \frac{1}{9}$$

110 Mathematics • Level E   Copying is illegal.   Peoples Common Core Mathematics

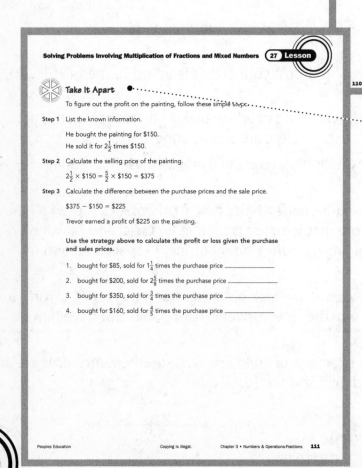

Solving Problems Involving Multiplication of Fractions and Mixed Numbers **27 Lesson**

Take It Apart

To figure out the profit on the painting, follow these simple steps.

Step 1 List the known information.

He bought the painting for $150.
He sold it for $2\frac{1}{2}$ times $150.

Step 2 Calculate the selling price of the painting.

$2\frac{1}{2} \times \$150 = \frac{5}{2} \times \$150 = \$375$

Step 3 Calculate the difference between the purchase prices and the sale price.

$\$375 - \$150 = \$225$

Trevor earned a profit of $225 on the painting.

Use the strategy above to calculate the profit or loss given the purchase and sales prices.

1. bought for $85, sold for $1\frac{1}{4}$ times the purchase price _____

2. bought for $200, sold for $2\frac{5}{8}$ times the purchase price _____

3. bought for $350, sold for $\frac{3}{4}$ times the purchase price _____

4. bought for $160, sold for $\frac{4}{5}$ times the purchase price _____

Take It Apart helps you solve a problem step-by-step to build your skills.

Put It Together asks you to apply the skill with different types of questions and activities.

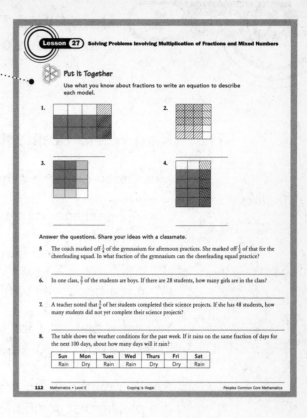

Put It Together

Use what you know about fractions to write an equation to describe each model.

1.

2.

3.

4.

Answer the questions. Share your ideas with a classmate.

5. The coach marked off $\frac{1}{4}$ of the gymnasium for afternoon practices. She marked off $\frac{1}{3}$ of that for the cheerleading squad. In what fraction of the gymnasium can the cheerleading squad practice?

6. In one class, $\frac{3}{7}$ of the students are boys. If there are 28 students, how many girls are in the class?

7. A teacher noted that $\frac{5}{6}$ of her students completed their science projects. If she has 48 students, how many students did not yet complete their science projects?

8. The table shows the weather conditions for the past week. If it rains on the same fraction of days for the next 100 days, about how many days will it rain?

Sun	Mon	Tues	Wed	Thurs	Fri	Sat
Rain	Dry	Rain	Rain	Dry	Dry	Rain

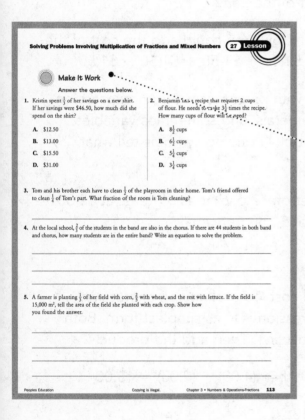

Make It Work

Answer the questions below.

1. Kristin spent $\frac{1}{3}$ of her savings on a new shirt. If her savings were $46.50, how much did she spend on the shirt?

   A. $12.50
   B. $13.00
   C. $15.50
   D. $31.00

2. Benjamin has a recipe that requires 2 cups of flour. He needs to make $3\frac{1}{4}$ times the recipe. How many cups of flour will he need?

   A. $8\frac{1}{2}$ cups
   B. $6\frac{1}{2}$ cups
   C. $5\frac{1}{4}$ cups
   D. $3\frac{1}{4}$ cups

3. Tom and his brother each have to clean $\frac{1}{2}$ of the playroom in their home. Tom's friend offered to clean $\frac{1}{4}$ of Tom's part. What fraction of the room is Tom cleaning?

4. At the local school, $\frac{2}{5}$ of the students in the band are also in the chorus. If there are 44 students in both band and chorus, how many students are in the entire band? Write an equation to solve the problem.

5. A farmer is planting $\frac{1}{3}$ of her field with corn, $\frac{2}{5}$ with wheat, and the rest with lettuce. If the field is 15,000 m², tell the area of the field she planted with each crop. Show how you found the answer.

Make It Work assesses your learning on the lesson skill with a variety of formats, including multiple-choice, short-answer, and extended-response questions.

Kick It Up end-of-chapter activities are fun projects to build your research, collaboration, problem-solving, technology, and writing skills.

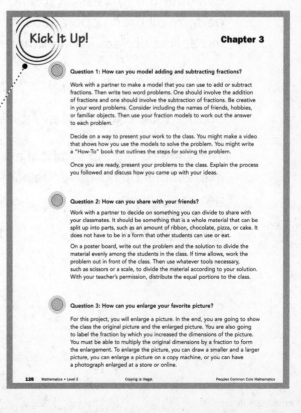

Kick It Up!   **Chapter 3**

Question 1: How can you model adding and subtracting fractions?

Work with a partner to make a model that you can use to add or subtract fractions. Then write two word problems. One should involve the addition of fractions and one should involve the subtraction of fractions. Be creative in your word problems. Consider including the names of friends, hobbies, or familiar objects. Then use your fraction models to work out the answer to each problem.

Decide on a way to present your work to the class. You might make a video that shows how you use the models to solve the problem. You might write a "How-To" book that outlines the steps for solving the problem.

Once you are ready, present your problems to the class. Explain the process you followed and discuss how you came up with your ideas.

Question 2: How can you share with your friends?

Work with a partner to decide on something you can divide to share with your classmates. It should be something that is a whole material that can be split up into parts, such as an amount of ribbon, chocolate, pizza, or cake. It does not have to be in a form that other students can use or eat.

On a poster board, write out the problem and the solution to divide the material evenly among the students in the class. If time allows, work the problem out in front of the class. Then use whatever tools necessary, such as scissors or a scale, to divide the material according to your solution. With your teacher's permission, distribute the equal portions to the class.

Question 3: How can you enlarge your favorite picture?

For this project, you will enlarge a picture. In the end, you are going to show the class the original picture and the enlarged picture. You are also going to label the fraction by which you increased the dimensions of the picture. You must be able to multiply the original dimensions by a fraction to form the enlargement. To enlarge the picture, you can draw a smaller and a larger picture, you can enlarge a picture on a copy machine, or you can have a photograph enlarged at a store or online.

5.0A.1   Use parentheses, brackets, or braces in numerical expressions, and evaluate expressions with these symbols.

Real World Connections

Mrs. Green buys the items below at the pet store.

     2 packages of rawhide treats @ 1 for $2.00

     6 cans of dog food @ 1 for $1.50

What is a good way to find the total cost of the items?

You know that "@ 1 for" means "at 1 item for." You could add the cost of the items: $2.00 + 2.00 + $1.50 + $1.50 + $1.50 + $1.50 + $1.50 + $1.50.

Another method is to use an expression with parentheses ( ). An **expression** is a phrase that combines operations, numerals, and sometimes variables. **Parentheses** are a type of grouping symbol. Grouping symbols tell what operation to perform first.

The expression below represents the cost of, "2 packages of treats at $2.00 per package" plus "6 cans of dog food at $1.50 per can."

     $(2 \times 2.00) + (6 \times 1.50)$

Evaluate the expression to find the total cost. To evaluate an expression, perform all of the operations so the expression is in its simplest form. Both multiplications are in parentheses. Multiply first. Then add the products.

     $2 \times 2.00 = 4.00$; $6 \times 1.50 = 9.00$; then $(4.00) + (9.00) = 13.00$

So, the total cost of the eight items is $13.00

Two other grouping symbols are **brackets** [ ] and **braces** { }. The three expressions below have the same value, 13. The only difference is the grouping symbol used.

     $(2 \times 2.00) + (6 \times 1.50)$ $[2 \times 2.00] + [6 \times 1.50]$ $\{2 \times 2.00\} + \{6 \times 1.50\}$

 ## Take It Apart

One box contains 24 packages of beads. Another box contains 16 packages of beads. Eight students take an equal number of packages from each box. Rita wrote a word expression and a numerical expression to represent the situation:

Word: 24 packages of beads plus 16 packages of beads divided evenly by 8 students

Numerical: $24 + 16 \div 8$

Step 1   Use a grouping symbol to show which operation to perform first. Since you add to find the total number of packages, group $24 + 16$.

$(24 + 16) \div 8$

Step 2   Evaluate the expression.

$(24 + 16) \div 8 =$

$(40) \div 8 =$

5   So each student took five packages.

There may be more than one expression that represents a situation. The expression below shows that you can divide first, and then add.

24 packages divided by 8 students plus 16 packages divided by 8 students =

$24 \div 8 + 16 \div 8$

$[24 \div 8] + [16 \div 8] =$ Step 1: Insert the grouping symbol.

$[3] + [2] =$ Step 2: Evaluate.

5   So each student took five packages.

Use the strategy above to answer each question. Insert a grouping symbol into the given expression. Then evaluate the expression.

1. A student ticket costs $4.00. Mr. Watson buys 23 student tickets. He pays with a $100 bill. How much change will he receive?

$100 - 23 \times 4$

2. Rita has 8 red counters and 6 blue counters. Robert has twice as many of each color counter. How many counters does he have?

$8 + 6 \times 2$

Put It Together

Use what you now know about using expressions with parentheses, brackets, and braces to answer each question below. First group the correct operations. Then evaluate the expression.

1. There are 6 students in a group. Each student has 4 sheets of white poster board and 8 sheets of colored poster board.

   $4 + 8 \times 6$

   How many sheets of poster board does the group have?

2. Carlos has 32 baseball cards. He gives 4 baseball cards to Connie and 7 to Ted.

   $32 - 4 + 7$

   How many baseball cards does Carlos have now?

3. Lakisha purchased 4 concert tickets online. Each ticket cost $12 each. There is a one-time fee of $5 for ordering online.

   $5 + 12 \times 4$

   What is the total cost of the four tickets?

4. A recipe calls for 3 cups of whole wheat flour and 7 cups of white flour. Kim wants to make only half the recipe.

   $3 + 7 \div 2$

   What is the total amount of flour she will use?

Answer each question. Discuss your answers with a classmate.

5. Zach has $25. He bought 6 cat's eye marbles for $3 each. How much money does he have left? Which expression below represents the given situation? Explain your thinking.

   $[25 - 6] \times 3$ $25 - (6 \times 3)$

   _____

   _____

6. Chandra gets $5 a week allowance. She also earns $7 an hour babysitting. Next week she will babysit for three hours. Chandra says she will earn $5 + 7 \times 3 = \$36$. Is she correct? Explain your answer.

   _____

   _____

Make It Work

Answer the questions below.

1. Robert needs to simplify this expression. Which operation should he do first?

$$12 - 6 + (2 \times 4) \div 2$$

A. $12 - 6$

B. $6 + 2$

C. 2×4

D. $4 \div 2$

2. There are 16 pens in one box and 12 pens in another box. Four students share the pens equally. Which expression correctly groups with the operation that is done first?

A. $16 \div (4 + 12) \div 4$

B. $(16 \div 4) + (12 \div 4)$

C. $16 + (12 \div 4)$

D. $(16 \div 4) + 12$

3. Anna mows lawns to earn extra money. This week she will mow 5 lawns and earn $20 per lawn. She has $10 now. She uses the expression $5 \times [20 + 10]$ and says she will have $150 next week.

   Is Anna correct? Use grouping symbols and evaluate an expression to explain your answer.

   _____

   _____

4. Explain how using grouping symbols could change the value of the expression $4 \times 3 + 6$.

   _____

   _____

5. Vivian says the three expressions below have the same value. Is she correct? Explain your answer.

   $8 + (15 - 5) + 2$ $8 + 15 - \{5 + 2\}$ $8 + [15 - 5] + 2$

   _____

   _____

   _____

Lesson 2 — Writing Numerical Expressions From Verbal Descriptions

5.OA.2 Write simple expressions that record calculations with numbers, and interpret numerical expressions without evaluating them.

Real World Connections

Rick has a collection of 120 baseball cards. Twelve of the cards are a second copy, or duplicate, of other cards. He gives away the duplicates. Now Rick has three times as many football cards as baseball cards. Write a math expression to represent the number of football cards he has.

○ First, write a verbal (word) description of the situation.

> Rick now has 3 times 120 baseball cards minus 12 cards given away.

○ Use the verbal description to write a numerical (math) expression. (Remember, a numerical **expression** is a combination of numbers and operation signs.) First, substitute operation signs for the words *times* and *minus*.

> Rick now has 3 × 120 baseball cards − 12 cards given away

○ Think: Do I need to do one of the operations first? Yes, subtract 120 − 12. This will tell the number of baseball cards Rick has now. Place parentheses around this operation. (Another way to think about this is to ask, "What will I multiply by 3?")

> Rick now has 3 × (120 baseball cards − 12 cards given away)

○ Remove the words.

> 3 × (120 − 12)

○ Compare the numerical expression to the verbal description to be certain they say the same thing.

3	times	120 baseball cards	minus	12 cards given away
3	×	(120	−	12)

Remember that it is important to use grouping symbols correctly.
(3 × 120) − 12 does not represent the situation described.

Take It Apart

Use the steps below to express this verbal description as a numerical expression.

Add 6 and 9, then divide by 3.

Step 1 Substitute operation signs for the words *add* and *divide by*.

6 + 9 then ÷ 3

Step 2 The word *then* tells you that you add before you divide. Use parentheses to show this.

(6 + 9) ÷ 3

Step 3 Compare the numerical expression to the verbal description to be certain they say the same thing.

Add	6	and	9	then	divide by	3.
	(6	+	9)		÷	3

Read each verbal description. Use the strategy above to write a numerical expression to represent the description. For items 3 and 4, write the word expression first. Then, write the numerical expression.

1. Subtract 6 from 10, then multiply by 5.

2. Divide 15 by 3, then multiply by 7.

3. Kathy has 3 gold markers and 5 silver markers. Her friend has twice as many of each color marker. Write an expression that represents the total number of markers her friend has.

4. Nelson buys 4 drawing tablets that cost $1.50 each. He gives the clerk a $10 bill. Write an expression that represents the amount of change he will receive.

Put It Together

Read each verbal description. Use what you know to express the description as a numerical expression only, without evaluating it. Hint: Some expressions may need two sets of grouping symbols.

1. Subtract 3 from 7, then multiply by 4.

2. Add 6 and 8, then divide by 2.

3. Multiply 3 times 3, then add 4 times 5.

4. Add 18 plus 7, then divide by 15 divided by 3.

5. There are 5 people in a room blowing up balloons. Then 3 more people arrive to help. Each person in the room blows up 4 balloons. Write an expression that represents the total number of balloons blown up.

6. There are 12 space stickers to a package and 10 ocean life stickers to a package. Deanna has 4 packages of space stickers and 3 packages of ocean life stickers. Write an expression that shows the total number of stickers Deanna has.

Answer each question. Discuss your answers with a classmate.

7. Calvin reads the description, "*Four times six plus five.*" He wants to write a numerical expression but isn't sure what to do. Explain why Calvin is confused. Then rewrite the description so it is clear.

8. A teacher writes this description on the board: *Add 4 and 3, then multiply by 5 minus 1*. A student writes it as: $(4 + 3) - (5 \times 1)$. Is the student's expression correct? Explain your answer.

Make It Work

Answer the questions below.

1. Express the following as a numerical expression.
"multiply 4 and 2, then add 6"

A. $4 \times (2 + 6)$

B. $4 + (2 \times 6)$

C. $(4 \times 2) + 6$

D. $(4 + 2) \times 6$

2. Describe the following verbally.
$(12 \div 4) \times 8$

A. multiply 8 times 4, then divide by 12

B. divide 12 by 4, then multiply by 8

C. multiply 4 times 12, then divide by 8

D. divide the sum of 4 and 8 by 12

3. Express the following as a numerical expression: multiply 4 boxes by 5, then subtract from 50 boxes.

_____

4. Read the verbal description below. Then write it as a numerical expression.

Tyrone stacked 4 sheets of blue paper and 2 sheets of green paper. Then he cut the stack of paper into three equal strips.

_____

5. Write a short verbal description of the situation below. Then write a numerical expression that can be used to find how much farther Carlo jogged.

Reba jogged 3 miles in the morning and 4 miles in the evening. Carlo jogged 5 miles in the morning and 6 miles in the evening.

_____

_____

5.0A.2 Write simple expressions that record calculations with numbers, and interpret numerical expressions without evaluating them.

Real World Connections

Kip wrote this expression. It represents the cost of three items and the change received when paid for with a $5 bill.

$$\$5.00 - (\$1.25 \times 3)$$

○ Write a verbal description of the expression. Start with the operation in parentheses.

($1.25 × 3) means *multiply* $1.25 *times* 3

$5.00 − means $5 *minus*

○ Put the phrases together so they match the meaning of the original expression. Use the word *then* to show that one operation is done *after* another operation.

multiply $1.25 *times* 3, *then* *subtract the product from* $5

○ There may be more than one way to write the verbal description. You also could say:

$5 *minus the product of* $1.25 *times* 3.

○ Check your verbal description.

1. Does it include all of the operations performed?

2. Does it clearly state the order in which the operations are performed?

Apply the Checklist A student wrote this description of Kip's expression: $5 *minus* $1.25 *times* 3. Check it against the list above. 1. Yes. 2. Oops! The expression does not clearly state the order for the operations. It could mean either *subtract, then multiply* OR *multiply, then subtract*.

Compare Two Values Suppose Kip paid with a $10 bill. Compare the values of the two expressions but do not evaluate them.

$$\$5.00 - (\$1.25 \times 3) \qquad \$10.00 - (\$1.25 \times 3)$$

Think: The same quantity is subtracted, but 10 > 5. The second expression has a greater value.

Take It Apart

Read the numerical expression below. Then write the expression using words.

$(6 + 4) \times (7 + 8) \div 5$

Step 1 Start with the operations in parentheses.

- $(6 + 4)$ means 6 *plus* 4
- $\times$ *means times*
- $(7 + 8)$ means 7 *plus* 8
- $\div 5$ means *divided by* 5

Step 2 Put the phrases together so they match the meaning of the original expression.

<u>Multiply</u> the <u>sum of 6 plus 4</u> by the <u>sum of 7 plus 8</u>. Then <u>divide the product by</u> 5.

Step 3 Use the checklist.

1. Does it include all of the operations performed? *Yes, multiply once, add twice, divide once*

2. Does it clearly state the order in which the operations are performed? *Yes*

Read each numerical expression. Then use the strategy above to write a verbal description that means the same thing.

1. $(5 + 3) \times 12$ 2. $8 - (3 + 2)$

Compare the values of each pair of expressions without evaluating them. Explain your thinking.

3. $8 \times (3,462 + 41)$ $3,462 + 41$

_____

4. $1,520 - (32 \div 8)$ $1,936 - (32 \div 8)$

_____

_____

Put It Together

Use what you know about interpreting numerical expressions to answer the following questions.

For questions 1 and 2, write a verbal description for the following numerical expressions.

1. $(25 - 15) \div 2$

_____

_____

2. $9 - (4 + 3)$

_____

_____

3. A truck is loaded with some bricks and some paving stones. The expression "873 + 912" represents the weight of the bricks and stones. A second truck is loaded with more bricks and stones. Use the expressions below to compare the weights of the loads on the first and the second truck.

Truck 1: $(873 + 912)$ Truck 2: $3 \times (873 + 912)$

_____

_____

4. A student reads the expression $5 \times (32 - 25)$ and writes this verbal description: *five times 32 minus 25*. Is the description accurate? Explain your answer.

_____

_____

5. Write a verbal description of each of the expressions below.

$23,000 + (573 - 128)$ $29,000 + (573 - 128)$

Without calculating their value, decide which expression has the greater value. Explain your reasoning.

_____

_____

Make It Work

Answer the questions below.

1. Which verbal description matches the numerical expression below?

   $(6 - 2) \times 7$

   A. six minus 2 times 7

   B. subtract 2 from 6, then multiply by 7

   C. multiply 7 times 2, then add 6

   D. multiply 6 times 7, then subtract 2

2. Which expression below has the greatest value?

   A. $5 \times (293 + 783)$

   B. $5 \times (293 + 283)$

   C. $4 \times (293 + 783)$

   D. $293 + 783$

3. Farmer Richards places 5 pounds of white potatoes and 3 pounds of red potatoes into a box. The expression "5 lb + 3 lb" represents the weight of the box. He needs 120 boxes to take to market. Write a verbal description of the weight of 120 identical boxes of potatoes.

_____

4. Reggie reads the expression $(5 \times 4) \div 2$. He expresses it as *five times four divided by 2*. Is Reggie's verbal description correct? Explain why or why not. If it isn't, rewrite the expression so it is correct.

_____

_____

5. Sonya bought some items and paid with a $20 bill. She wrote the expression below to represent the cost and the change she received.

   $$\$20.00 - (\$2 \times 2) + (\$1.50 \times 4) + (\$3 \times 3)$$

   ◦ Write a verbal description of Sonya's expression.

   ◦ Write another numerical expression that shows paying with a $50 bill.

   ◦ Compare the values of the two expressions without evaluating them.

_____

_____

_____

Lesson 4 Generating Numerical Patterns

5.0A.3 Generate two numerical patterns using two given rules. Identify apparent relationships between corresponding terms. Form ordered pairs consisting of corresponding terms from the two patterns, and graph the ordered pairs on a coordinate plane. *For example, given the rule "Add 3" and the starting number 0, and given the rule "Add 6" and the starting number 0, generate terms in the resulting sequences, and observe that the terms in one sequence are twice the corresponding terms in the other sequence. Explain informally why this is so.*

Real World Connections

Key Words

numerical
 pattern

rule

term

multiple

A **numerical pattern** is a list of numbers that follow a rule. The **rule** tells the relationship between the numbers. Each number in the list is a **term** of the pattern. The symbol … at the end of a patterns shows that the pattern continues.

The numerical pattern below starts with 0 and follows the rule "Add 5." This means you add 5 to the value of a term to find the next term. This is the same pattern you say if you count by 5s: 5, 10, 15, 20, 25, … .

Add 5: (0 + 5 = **5**), (5 + 5 = **10**), (10 + 5 = **15**), (15 + 5 = **20**),
(20 + 5 = **25**), …

Numerical patterns apply to everyday life. For example, two clocks both chime at midnight. Clock 1 will chime again every 4 hours. Clock 2 will chime every 6 hours. When will they chime again at the same time? Clock 1 follows the rule "Add 4." Clock 2 follows the rule "Add 6."

Term   1st 2nd 3rd 4th 5th 6th
Add 4:   4, 8, <u>12</u>, 16, 20, <u>24</u>, …
Add 6:   6, <u>12</u>, 18, <u>24</u>, …

There are 24 hours in a day, so the terms stop with the number 24. The numbers 12 and 24 are terms in both patterns. Both clocks will chime at 12 noon (12 hours) and again at 12 midnight (24 hours). A number line shows this. When the circle and triangle are on the same number, the clocks chime together.

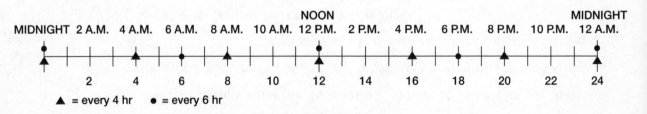

▲ = every 4 hr   ● = every 6 hr

Remember, a **multiple** is the product of a given number and another number. Twelve and 24 are multiplies of both 4 and 6. They are also the product of the number in the rule and the term number. For example, in "Add 4", the given number is 4. 4 × 3rd term = 4 × 3 = 12.

Take It Apart

Use the rules "Add 3" and "Add 6" to write the first 8 terms in 2 numerical patterns.

Step 1 Start both patterns with zero. Apply the rules.

Add 3:
$0 + 3 = \underline{3}$, $3 + 3 = \underline{6}$, $6 + 3 = \underline{9}$, $9 + 3 = \underline{12}$, $12 + 3 = \underline{15}$, $15 + 3 = \underline{18}$, $18 + 3 = \underline{21}$, $21 + 3 = \underline{24}$

Add 6:
$0 + 6 = \underline{6}$, $6 + 6 = \underline{12}$, $12 + 6 = \underline{18}$, $18 + 6 = \underline{24}$, $24 + 6 = \underline{30}$, $30 + 6 = \underline{36}$, $36 + 6 = \underline{42}$, $42 + 6 = \underline{48}$

Step 2 Identify any numbers that appear in both patterns.

Add 3: 3, <u>6</u>, 9, <u>12</u>, 15, <u>18</u>, 21, <u>24</u> …

Add 6: <u>6</u>, <u>12</u>, <u>18</u>, <u>24</u>, 30, 36, 42, 48, …

The numbers 6, 12, 18, and 24 appear in both patterns.

Step 3 Why is this true? Notice 6, 12, 18, and 24 are divisible by both 3 and 6. This is why they appear in both patterns.

1. Look at the numerical patterns below. Do any numbers appear in both patterns? Explain why or why not.

    Add 6: 6, 12, 18, 24, 30, 36, 42, 48, …

    Add 5: 5, 10, 15, 20, 25, 30, 35, 40…

    _____

2. Use the strategy above to answer the question. Write the first six terms in two number patterns. Use the rules "Add 5" and "Add 8". Do any numbers appear in both patterns? Explain why or why not.

    _____

    _____

3. Two buzzers start at the same time. One will buzz every 3 minutes. The other will buzz every 5 minutes. In how many minutes will they both buzz at the same time? Use number patterns to answer the question.

    _____

Put It Together

Use what you now know about numerical patterns to answer questions 1 and 2.

1. Write the first 6 terms in a pattern that follows the rule "Add 10".

2. What is the 5th term in a pattern that follows the rule "Add 9"?

_____

_____

3. Four students will write the first five terms of a numerical pattern. They each have a different rule.

      "Add 15"   "Add 3"   "Add 10"   "Add 5"

The first five terms of which patterns will include the number 15? Explain why.

_____

_____

4. Use the rules "Add 10" and "Add 25" to write the first eight terms in two numerical patterns. Identify the numbers that appear in both patterns.

_____

_____

5. Kelly and Jay jog every day. They like to vary the routes that take. Kelly jogs around the pond every 3 days. Jay jogs around the pond every 7 days. Complete the numerical patterns below. Then answer the questions.

Add 3: 3, 6, 9, ___, ___, ___, ___, ___, ___, ___ ···

Add 5: 5, 10, 15, ___, ___, ___, ___

In the "Add 3" pattern, what does the number 15 represent?

_____

Kelly and Jay will both jog around the pond every _____ days. Explain your reasoning.

_____

_____

Make It Work

Answer the questions below.

1. What number will be the 10th term in the pattern below?

5, 10, 15, 20, 25, 30, …

A. 40   **B.** 45

C. 50   **D.** 55

2. Which pattern starts at zero and follows the rule "Add 8"?

A. 4, 8, 12, 20, 28, …

B. 4, 12, 20, 28, 36

C. 8, 16, 32, 64, 128, …

D. 8, 16, 24, 32, 40, 48, …

3. Explain what it means if the rule for a pattern is "Add 2." Include the word *term* in your explanation. Then write the first 5 terms of a pattern that starts with zero and follows this rule. Remember to show that the pattern continues.

4. Two different patterns start with zero. One follows the rule "Add 6." The other follows the rule "Add 12." Predict if any numbers will appear in both patterns within the first five terms. Write the first five terms in both patterns. Was your prediction correct? Explain.

5. There are door prizes at the school fair. Every 8th person who enters will receive a backpack. Every 10th person will receive a calculator. There are 6 backpacks and 3 calculators to give away. Will anyone receive a calculator and a backpack?

○ Use numerical patterns to answer the question. What two rules should you use? Write the first six terms for each pattern.

○ Answer the question. Explain your answer. (Remember, there are only 3 calculators and 6 backpacks.)

Lesson 5 — Identifying Relationships Between Numerical Patterns

5.0A.3 Generate two numerical patterns using two given rules. Identify apparent relationships between corresponding terms. Form ordered pairs consisting of corresponding terms from the two patterns, and graph the ordered pairs on a coordinate plane. *For example, given the rule "Add 3" and the starting number 0, and given the rule "Add 6" and the starting number 0, generate terms in the resulting sequences, and observe that the terms in one sequence are twice the corresponding terms in the other sequence. Explain informally why this is so.*

Real World Connections

Tool
calculator

Key Words

corresponding
terms

sequence

equivalent
fractions

Maya and William have these numerical patterns.

Maya's Pattern   2, 4, 6, 8, 10, 12, …

William's Pattern   4, 8, 12, 16, 20, 24, …

They need to find the rule for each pattern. The following will help them.

○ Do the values increase or decrease? *increase*

○ What operations increase the value of a number? *addition and multiplication*

○ What is the difference between adjacent terms?

  Maya: $4 - 2 = $ **2**, $6 - 4 = $ **2**, $8 - 6 = $ **2**, $10 - 8 = $ **2**, $12 - 10 = $ **2**
    difference of 2

  William: $8 - 4 = $ **4**, $12 - 8 = $ **4**, $16 - 12 = $ **4**, $20 - 16 = $ **4**, $24 - 20 = $ **4**
    difference of 4

○ State the rule.

  Maya's pattern increases by 2 units. William's pattern increases by 4 units. They are addition patterns, with rules "Add 2" and "Add 4".

Corresponding terms are terms that occupy the same position in a list of numbers, or **sequence**. In the patterns above, 6 and 12 are the 3rd terms in each sequence. They are corresponding terms. Compare them.

○ The terms in the "Add 4" sequence are twice the value of the corresponding terms in the "Add 2" sequence.

○ A fraction formed from corresponding terms in the two sequences simplifies to $\frac{1}{2}$, as shown below. The numerator is a term from the first pattern. The denominator is the corresponding term from the second pattern. The fractions name the same amount so they are **equivalent fractions**.

$$\frac{4}{8} = \frac{4 \div 4}{8 \div 4} = \frac{1}{2} \qquad \frac{6}{12} = \frac{6 \div 6}{12 \div 6} = \frac{1}{2}$$

Take It Apart

Identify relationships between the two numerical patterns below.

Step 1 First, find the rule for each pattern. Look at the terms in each sequence.

Pattern 1:   ..., 9, 12, 15, 18, 21, ...
Pattern 2:   ..., 15, 20, 25, 30, 35, ...

Ask: Do the values of the terms increase or decrease? *increase*
          What operations increase the value of a number? *addition and multiplication*

Step 2 Find the difference between adjacent terms.

$12 - 9 = \mathbf{3}$, $15 - 12 = \mathbf{3}$, $18 - 15 = \mathbf{3}$, $21 - 18 = \mathbf{3}$ *difference of* 3
$20 - 15 = \mathbf{5}$, $25 - 20 = \mathbf{5}$, $30 - 25 = \mathbf{5}$, $35 - 30 = \mathbf{5}$ *difference of* 5

Step 3 State the rules.

The rule for Pattern 1 is "Add 3". The rule for Pattern 2 is "Add 5".

Step 4 Compare the corresponding terms of the two patterns. Subtract the pattern numbers above to compare.

○ $15 - 9 = 6$ $20 - 12 = 8$ $25 - 15 = 10$ $30 - 18 = 12$ $35 - 21 = 14$

The difference between the terms is increasing.

○ Write a fraction to compare the two patterns. Simplify the fraction.

$$\frac{9}{15} = \frac{9 \div 3}{15 \div 3} = \frac{3}{5}$$

The relationship between the corresponding terms is 3 to 5. Try another fraction to confirm it.

Use the steps above to answer each question. Use your calculator if you wish.

1. Identify the rule for this pattern: _____, 16, 24, 32, 40, 48, ...

2. Identify the rule for the pattern: _____, 20, 30, 40, 50, 60, ...

Identify any relationships you see between these two patterns.

_____

_____

Put It Together

Use your calculator and what you now know about identifying relationships between numerical patterns to answer each question.

1. Identify the rule for this pattern:

..., 14, 21, 28, 35, 42, ...

_____

2. Name two corresponding terms in these two numerical patterns.

5, 10, 15, 20, 25, ...
6, 12, 18, 24, 30, ...

_____

3. Look at the pattern below.

4, 8, 12, 16, 20, 24, __, __, ...

Describe how you could use the rule for the pattern to find the missing terms. Then find the missing terms.

_____

_____

_____

4. Compare the patterns below. Identify any relationships you see between the corresponding terms.

3, 6, 9, 12, 15, ...   9, 18, 27, 36, 45, ...

_____

_____

_____

5. Each bracelet Janice makes has 3 gold beads and 6 red beads. If Janice has 36 red beads to use, how many gold beads will she need? Show your work. (Hint: Use the concept of corresponding terms.)

_____

_____

Make It Work

Answer the questions below.

1. Look at the terms in the sequence below. What is the rule for the pattern?

..., 16, 24, 32, 40, 48, ...

A. Add 2   **B.** Add 4

C. Add 8   **D.** Add 16

2. What term in the second sequence corresponds to the 35 in the first sequence?

5, 10, 15, 20, 25, 30, 35, 40...

6, 12, 18, 24, 30, 36, 42, 48, ...

A. 5   **B.** 25

C. 40   **D.** 42

3. Compare the patterns below. Identify any relationships you see between the corresponding terms.

8, 16, 24, 32, 40, ...   9, 18, 27, 36, 45, ...

_____

_____

4. Look at the pattern to the right.   ___, ___, 33, 44, 55, 66, __, ...

Find the rule for the pattern. Then, find the missing terms using the rule. Explain your method.

_____

_____

5. Some students are making tote bags to sell at a fundraiser. The patterns below show the total number of decorative buttons and tassels needed for five tote bags.

    Buttons: 3, 6, 9, 12, 15   Tassels: 4, 8, 12, 16, 20

○ How many buttons and tassels are needed for six tote bags?

_____

○ Explain how you can use corresponding terms to find the number of buttons needed for 25 tote bags.

_____

○ The students have 38 buttons and 120 tassels. They say they can make 30 tote bags. Are the students correct? Why or why not? Use what you know about numerical patterns to support your answer.

_____

_____

Question 1: What does it mean to write an expression?

Expressions are combinations of number and operation signs. When you read the expression, you say it in words. For example, 4 + 2 means *four plus two*. Develop a game where students match numeric and word expressions. Here is a suggested game but you can make up your own game and rules.

Make a set of at least fifteen numerical expressions on plain index cards. On colored index cards write a verbal expression for each one. Divide the numerical cards among the players. Turn the verbal cards face down on the table. Each player, in turn, turns over a verbal expression. If it matches a card in his or her hand, the player keeps it. If not, the player turns it back over. Continue playing until there are no cards left on the table. The player with the most pairs wins.

Once you decide on the rules for your game, write them on a piece of paper so the players can see them. Think about how you will play: Will each player take only one turn at a time? Will a player get another turn if he or she finds a matching pair? What will you do if there is a tie?

Question 2: Can different expressions mean the same thing?

The expression $(5 + 2) \times 3$ means the same thing as $3 \times (5 + 2)$. It does not mean the same thing as $5 + (2 \times 3)$ or $5 + 2 \times 3$. This may seem confusing but parentheses can help you understand what operations to perform first.

Make two identical sets of each type of large card—digits (0–9), signs (+, −, ×, ÷, =, and ≠), and parentheses. They don't have to be fancy, just big. One way to make them is to type them on the computer and print them out. Then cut out each one and paste or tape it on a cardboard square. Use a different color cardboard for each type of card. Use the cards to make an expression.

Then challenge a classmate to make another expression that means the same thing. Or make two expressions and challenge a classmate to decide whether they mean the same thing.

Chapter 1

Question 3: How can you generate number patterns?

It could be very handy to have a machine that generates number patterns. Why not make one? Think of a rule for a pattern, say, "Add 4." On a long strip of paper, write the first twelve numbers in the pattern "Add 4." Then design a "machine" you can slide the strip through. Make a place on it that shows the rule. Here is one design but you can be inventive and make any devise that works.

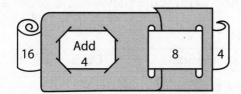

If you would like, work with a partner. Make number strips for at least ten rules—Add 3, Subtract 2, Multiply by 4, Divide by 5, and so on. Use number facts to help you. When you are finished, present your pattern machine to the class and explain how it works.

Question 4: What are corresponding terms in number patterns?

It can be difficult to explain the concept of *corresponding terms* in words alone. A good visual image will help a lot.

Draw a graphic cartoon in which one student explains the concept to another student. Define the meaning of *corresponding terms*. Then use graphic images to support the explanation. Write your script first. The script tells what you will say. Draw a sketch of the graphics. Before you make your final project, present the script and graphics to a classmate. Ask him or her whether your presentation is clear. Make any needed changes before making the final product.

Lesson 6 Understanding the Meaning of Place Value

5.NBT.1 Recognize that in a multi-digit number, a digit in one place represents 10 times as much as it represents in the place to its right and $\frac{1}{10}$ of what it represents in the place to its left.

Real World Connections

The college football stadium in Wayne's town can seat 32,283 people. To understand what this number means, you need to understand place value.

A **digit** is a symbol used to write a number. The digits you use are 0, 1, 2, 3, 4, 5, 6, 7, 8, and 9. The value of a digit, or its **place value**, depends on its position (place) in the number. A **place-value chart** shows the order and the names of the different places.

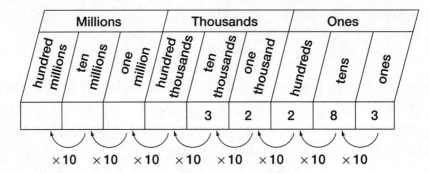

The number system you use is based on groups of ten.

○ The value of the places *increases* from right to left. For any place, the place to its *left* has a value that is 10 times greater.

○ The values *decrease* from left to right. For any place, the place to its *right* has a value that is $\frac{1}{10}$ as great.

Look at the number in the place-value chart. The digit 2 appears twice: 32,253. What are the values of 2? How are they related?

○ Look at the 2 in the hundreds place. Its value is 2 hundreds or 200. To its left is a 2 in the thousands place. Its value is 2 thousand, or 2,000. The value of the 2 in the thousands place is 10 times greater than the value of the 2 in the hundreds place: $200 \times 10 = 2,000$.

○ Look at the 2 in the thousands place. To its right is a 2 in the hundreds place. The value of the 2 in the hundreds place is $\frac{1}{10}$ the value of the 2 in the thousands place. $2,000 \times \frac{1}{10} = 2,000 \div 10 = 200$ (Remember, $\times \frac{1}{10}$ is the same as $\div 10$.)

The digit 3 appears twice—in the ones place and in the ten thousands place. How much greater is 3 ten thousands than 3 ones? Count the number of places from ones to ten thousands—4 places. 3 ten thousands is $10 \times 10 \times 10 \times 10$ times greater than 3 ones.

Take It Apart

Use what you know about place value, your calculator, and a blank place value chart to identify the values of 5 in the number 35,525.

Step 1 Underline each 5. Tell what it means in each place. 3<u>5</u>,<u>5</u>2<u>5</u>   From left to right the values are: 5 thousand, 5 hundred, 5 ones

Step 2 ○ Look at the 5 in the thousands place: 3<u>5</u>,525. Then look at the 5 to its right.

○ Is 5 thousand 10 × *greater than* or $\frac{1}{10}$ *the value* of 5 hundred?

○ Any place is 10 × greater than the place to its right. 5,000 is 10 × greater than 500.

Step 3 ○ Look at the 5 in the hundreds place: 35,<u>5</u>25. Then look at the 5 to its left.

○ Is 5 hundred 10 × *greater than* or $\frac{1}{10}$ *the value* of 5 thousand?

○ Any place is $\frac{1}{10}$ the value of the place to its left. 500 is $\frac{1}{10}$ the value of 5,000.

Step 4 How is the 5 in the ones place related to the values above? Count the distances between the places on your place value chart. Use your calculator to multiply or divide.

Compare 5 and 500.

○ 5 ones is two places to the right of 5 hundreds. It is $\frac{1}{10} \times \frac{1}{10}$, or $\frac{1}{100}$, the value of 500.

500 ÷ 100 = 5

○ 5 hundreds is two places to the left of 5 ones. It is 10 × 10, or 100 times, the value of 5.

5 × 100 = 500

Compare 5 and 5,000.

○ 5 ones is three places to the right of 5 thousands. It is $\frac{1}{10} \times \frac{1}{10} \times \frac{1}{10}$, or $\frac{1}{1,000}$, the value of 5,000.

5,000 ÷ 1,000 = 5

○ 5 thousands is three places to the left of 5 ones. It is 10 × 10 × 10, or 1,000 times, the value of 5.

5 × 1,000 = 5,000

Use what you know about place value to answer the questions below.

1. Look at the number 458,338. What two values does the digit 3 have in this number?

_____

2. Look at the number 45,528,947. Is the 5 in the hundred thousands place 10 × or $\frac{1}{10}$ of the value of the 5 in the millions place? Explain your answer.

_____

Put It Together

For questions 1 and 2, use "10 ×" or "$\frac{1}{10}$" to finish each statement.

1. The thousands place has _____ the value of the ten thousands place.

2. The ten millions place has _____ the value of the one millions place.

3. Look at this number: 152,779,802

   What is the place value of the 7 on the left?

   What is the place value of the 7 on the right?

For questions 4 and 5, use this number: 36,662,462

4. Find the digit in the hundred thousands place. Which digit has $\frac{1}{10}$ the value of this digit?
   Support your answer.

   _____

   _____

5. Find the digit in the thousands place. Compare the value of this digit with the digit in the ones
   place. Support your answer.

   _____

   _____

   _____

6. The same rules apply to decimal numbers. Look at the decimal place values below.
   Is 5 tenths $\frac{1}{10}$ of or 10 × 5 hundredths? Explain your answer.

ones	.	tenths	hundredths	thousandths
5		5	5	5

   _____

   _____

 ## Make It Work

Answer the questions below.

1. What is the place value of 4 in the number 246,375,020?

   A. 4 hundred millions

   B. 4 ten millions

   C. 4 millions

   D. 4 hundred thousands

2. Which describes the value of the place to the right of the underlined digit? 60,4<u>8</u>8,034

   A. $\frac{1}{10}$ its value

   B. $10 \times$ its value

   C. $\frac{1}{10} \times \frac{1}{10}$ its value

   D. 10×10 its value

3. Tara has two checks. One is for $328.45. The other is for $297.99. Tara's friend says that $297.99 has a greater value because it has a lot of 9s in it. Is her friend correct? Explain your answer.

   _____

   _____

   _____

4. Jason has the number 452.202. The number contains 2 tenths. What value in the number is 10 times this value? Explain your answer.

   _____

5. Look at the number 3,730,238.

   The digit 2 has a value of 2 hundreds. What are the values of the 3s?

   _____

   Which 3 is 10×10 greater than 3 ten thousands. Explain you answer.

   _____

   _____

   Which 3 is $\frac{1}{10} \times \frac{1}{10} \times \frac{1}{10} \times \frac{1}{10} \times \frac{1}{10}$ of another 3? Explain your answer.

   _____

   _____

Lesson 7 · Using Exponents to Represent Powers of 10

5.NBT.2 Explain patterns in the number of zeros of the product when multiplying a number by powers of 10, and explain patterns in the placement of the decimal point when a decimal is multiplied or divided by a power of 10. Use whole-number exponents to denote powers of 10.

Real World Connections

Toolbox

calculator

Key Words

exponent

base

factor

power of 10

standard form

Jason went to a photography exhibit. It featured photos of small objects that are greatly enlarged. One photo is of a tiny insect that is 2 millimeter (mm) in length. The photo enlarges it 10^3 times. To understand what this means, you need to understand the meaning of 10^3.

The number 10^3 is in exponential form. The small 3 to the upper right of 10 is the exponent. An **exponent** tells the number of times the **base** is used as a **factor**. In this number, the base 10 is used as a factor three times.

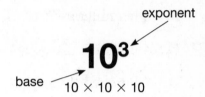

A power is the value of an exponent in an expression. When the base is 10, the number is called a **power of 10**. Read the number 10^3 as, "ten to the third power" or "ten to the power of 3."

There is a pattern to the number of zeros in powers of ten. Look at the table below. The exponent represents the number of zeros in the standard form of the number. Each digit of a number in **standard form** is in a place value. Each time the exponent increases by 1, the number of zeros increases by 1.

Powers of 10

Exponential Form	Factors	Standard Form
$10^1 =$	10	10 (1 zero)
$10^2 =$	10×10	100 (2 zeros)
$10^3 =$	$10 \times 10 \times 10$	1,000 (3 zeros)
$10^4 =$	$10 \times 10 \times 10 \times 10$	10,000 (4 zeros)
$10^5 =$	$10 \times 10 \times 10 \times 10 \times 10$	100,000 (5 zeros)
$10^6 =$	$10 \times 10 \times 10 \times 10 \times 10 \times 10$	1,000,000 (6 zeros)

What does the enlargement of the photograph mean? The actual length of the insect, 2 mm, is enlarged 10^3 times. This means 2 mm is multiplied by 1,000 or by $10 \times 10 \times 10$. A shorthand way to write this is 2×10^3.

Another photo shows a virus that is enlarged $10 \times 10 \times 10 \times 10 \times 10 \times 10 \times 10$, or 10,000,000 times. To express this quantity as a power of 10, count the zeros. The photo is enlarged 10^7 times.

 Peoples Common Core Mathematics

Take It Apart

Use what you know about powers of 10 and exponents to represent powers of 10. You may use a calculator to help you.

Yumi has the number 100,000. How can she express it as a power of 10?

Step 1   Count the number of zeros in the number. There are 5 zeros.

Step 2   Write the base: 10

Step 3   There are 5 zeros. Use 5 as the exponent: 10^5

Step 4   Read the number as, "ten to the fifth power" or "ten to the power of five."

Yumi also has the expression $10 \times 10 \times 10 \times 10 \times 10 \times 10 \times 10 \times 10$.

How can she express it as a power of 10?

Step 1   Count the number of times 10 is used as a factor. It is used 8 times.

Step 2   Write the base: 10

Step 3   Ten is a factor 8 times. Use 8 as the exponent: 10^8

Step 4   Read the number as, "ten to the eighth power" or "ten to the power of eight."

Use what you know about place value to answer the questions below.

1. Express the number 10,000,000 in exponential form. _____

2. Express the number $10 \times 10 \times 10 \times 10$ in exponential form. _____

3. Express the number 10^9 in standard form. Explain your method.

   _____

   _____

4. Express the number 10^5 as the product of factors. Explain your method.

   _____

   _____

5. Kevin has this expression: $4 \times 1,000$. How can he write it using a power of 10? Explain your reasoning.

   _____

   _____

Put It Together

Follow the steps you learned to represent powers of 10.

1. Identify the base and the exponent in the number 10^6.

   _____

2. In the number 10^3, what does the exponent mean?

   _____

3. Express 10,000,000 as a power of ten. _____

4. Express $10 \times 10 \times 10 \times 10 \times 10$ in exponential form. _____

5. Use words to describe the meaning of the expression 5×10^3.

   _____

6. Write 10^{10} in standard form. (Remember the pattern of zeros in powers of 10.)

   _____

7. Some scientists estimate that there are 100 billion stars in the Milky Way galaxy. In standard form, 100 billion is 100,000,000,000. Write 100 billion in exponential form.

   _____

8. Katlin does not understand the difference between 10^3 and 3^{10}. Use what you know about bases, exponents, and powers of ten to explain the difference.

   _____

   _____

Make It Work

Answer the questions below.

1. Which is 1,000,000 in exponential form?

 A. 10^4

 B. 10^5

 C. 10^6

 D. 10^7

2. Which means the same thing as 10^8?

 A. 1,000,000

 B. 80,000,000,000

 C. $8 \times 8 \times 8 \times 8 \times 8 \times 8 \times 8 \times 8 \times 8 \times 8$

 D. $10 \times 10 \times 10 \times 10 \times 10 \times 10 \times 10 \times 10$

3. Brandon says that $10^1 = 100$. Is he correct? Explain why or why not.

_____

_____

_____

4. Write the expression $10 \times 10 \times 10 \times 10 \times 10 \times 10$ in standard, in exponential, and in word form.

_____

_____

5. Which number below can be expressed as a power of ten in exponential form? Explain your answer. Include the number in exponential form in your answer.

$5 \times 5 \times 5 \times 5 \times 5 \times 5 \times 5 \times 5 \times 5 \times 5$ $10 \times 10 \times 10 \times 10 \times 10$

_____

_____

_____

_____

5.NBT.2   Explain patterns in the number of zeros of the product when multiplying a number by powers of 10, and explain patterns in the placement of the decimal point when a decimal is multiplied or divided by a power of 10. Use whole-number exponents to denote powers of 10.

Real World Connections

Key Words

expanded form

factor

products

A busy restaurant sells 8 ounce-servings of orange juice at breakfast. One week they sold 1,000 servings. How many ounces of orange juice is this?

To answer this question, multiply $8 \times 1,000$. When you write 1,000 in **expanded form** it is easy to see that it is a power of 10.

$$8 \times 1,000 = 8 \times 10 \times 10 \times 10 = 8 \times 10^3$$

Ten is a **factor** three times. To multiply $8 \times 1,000$, add 3 zeros to the right of 8. $8 \times 1,000 = 8,000$. The restaurant sold 8,000 ounces of orange juice.

○ When multiplying powers of 10, there is a pattern to the number of zeros in the **products**. The number of zeros in the product is equal to the number of zeros in the power of 10. Each time the power of 10 increases by one zero, the product increases by one zero.

$8 \times 1 = 8$	no zeros
$8 \times 10 = 80$	one zero
$8 \times 100 = 800$	two zeros
$8 \times 1,000 = 8,000$	three zeros
$8 \times 10,000 = 80,000$	four zeros

○ The rule also is true for powers of 10 expressed in exponential form.

$8 \times 10^5 = 800,000$ The exponent is 5. Place 5 zeros to the right of 8.

○ The rule also applies when you multiply two numbers that are powers of 10.

$10 \times 1,000,000 = 10,000,000$ There are 6 zeros in 1,000,000. Place 6 zeros to the right of 10.

$10 \times 10^6 = 10,000,000$ The exponent is 6. Place 6 zeros to the right of 10.

Adding zeros is the same as changing the position of the decimal point. Look at the equation on the right: $74 \times 1,000,000$. There are 6 zeros in 1,000,000. The decimal point moves 6 places to the right,

$74 \times 1,000,000 = 74.\underset{\smile\smile\smile\smile\smile\smile}{000000}.$

Take It Apart

To multiply a whole number by a power of 10 that is in **standard form,** use the steps below.

Step 1 Count the number of zeros in the power of 10: $15 \times 1,000$
There are three zeros in 1,000. 10 is a factor 3 times.

Step 2 Add the same number of zeros to the right of 15: $15 \times 1,000 = 15\,\underline{0}\,\underline{0}\,\underline{0}$

Step 3 Insert a comma into the product: $15 \times 1,000 = 15,000$

To multiply a whole number by a power of 10 that is in **exponential form,** use the steps below.

Step 1 Identify the exponent. 28×10^5
The exponent is 5. 10 is a factor 5 times.

Step 2 Add 5 zeros to the right of the 28: $28 \times 10^5 = 28\,\underline{0}\,\underline{0}\,\underline{0}\,\underline{0}\,\underline{0}$

Step 3 Insert commas into the product: $28 \times 10^5 = 2,800,000$

Use the steps above and what you know about patterns of zeros to answer the following items.

1. Express the product in standard form. $35 \times 1,000,000$ _____

2. Express the product in standard form. 6×10^7 _____

3. Find the product of 382×100 by moving the decimal point in 382. Explain what you did.

    _____

    _____

4. Aram says that $40 \times 10,000 = 40,000$. Is he correct? If not, what mistake did he likely make?

    _____

5. The closest the planet Mars gets to Earth is about 55×10^6 kilometers. Use patterns of zero to express the product in standard form. Explain your reasoning.

    _____

Put It Together

Use what you know about patterns of zeros in products of powers of 10 to answer the following items.

1. How many times is 10 a factor in this multiplication: $4 \times 100,000$. _____

2. How many times is 10 a factor in this multiplication: 5×10^7 _____

3. $100 \times 10,000 =$ ___ $10,000 \times 100 =$ ___ Use patterns of zeros to tell if the products will be the same or different. Explain your answer.

_____

_____

_____

4. The distance between Earth and the Moon varies. The closest distance is about 36×10^4 kilometers. What is this distance in standard form?

_____

_____

5. In the problem $12 \times 1,000$ why is adding 3 zeros to 12 the same as moving the decimal point in 12 three places to the right?

_____

_____

6. A student has the problems below. The student thinks she sees a rule for how to multiply two powers of 10 that are in exponential form.

$100 \times 1,000 = 100,000$ $10^2 \times 10^3 = 10^5$
$100 \times 10,000 = 1,000,000$ $10^2 \times 10^4 = 10^6$

What is the rule? Why do you think the rule works?

_____

_____

Make It Work

Answer the questions below.

1. $14 \times 100{,}000 =$ ___

    A. 14,000   **B.** 140,000

    C. 1,400,000   **D.** 14,000,000

2. $11 \times 10^3 =$ ___

    A. 1000   **B.** 11,000

    C. 110,000   **D.** 111,000

3. Show two different ways to solve $92 \times 1{,}000$. Explain why each method works.

_____

_____

_____

_____

4. Janet says that $10 \times 10^5 = 10 \times 10 \times 10 \times 10 \times 10$, or 100,000. Barry does not agree. Which student is correct? Use patterns of zeros to support your answer.

_____

_____

_____

5. David reads this statement in his math book, "When you multiply by powers of 10, there is a pattern to the number of zeros in the products."

    ○ Explain what this statement means. Include some examples in you explanation.

    ○ How are exponents related to the statement?

_____

_____

_____

_____

_____

Explaining Patterns in the Placement of the Decimal Point

5.NBT.2 Explain patterns in the number of zeros of the product when multiplying a number by powers of 10, and explain patterns in the placement of the decimal point when a decimal is multiplied or divided by a power of 10. Use whole-number exponents to denote powers of 10.

Real World Connections

Key Words

decimal number

power of 10

Mr. and Mrs. Akins own a party store. They receive an order for 100 packages of glow necklaces. Each package of four necklaces costs $4.99. Mrs. Atkins mentally calculates the total cost as $499. What process might she have used?

The number 4.99 is a **decimal number**. It contains a decimal point and a value in the tenths place and the hundredths place. Mrs. Akins multiplied $4.99 × 100 by moving the decimal point two places to the right.

When you *multiply* a decimal number by 10, the product is ten times *greater than* the number multiplied. When you multiply by 100, the product is 100 times greater.

$0.35 × 10 = 3.5$ There is one zero in 10. The decimal point moves 1 place to the right.

$0.35 × 100 = 35$ There are two zeros in 100. The decimal point moves 2 places to the right.

Look at the pattern formed when multiplying a decimal by a **power of 10.** The position of the decimal point moves one place to the *right* for every zero in the power of 10.

$4.99 × 1 =$ 4.99
$4.99 × 10 =$ 49.90
$4.99 × 100 =$ 499.00
$4.99 × 1,000 =$ $4,990.00$
$4.99 × 10,000 = 49,900.00$

Look at the pattern formed when dividing a decimal by a power of 10. The position of the decimal point moves one place to the *left* for every zero in the power of 10.

$2.8 ÷ 1 =$ 2.8
$2.8 ÷ 10 =$ 0.28
$2.8 ÷ 100 =$ 0.028
$2.8 ÷ 1,000 = 0.0028$

You might need to add zeros to the left of a number before you can move the decimal point to the correct position.

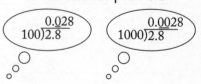

Understanding these two concepts will make it easy to multiply and divide any decimal number by a power of ten.

               Peoples Common Core Mathematics

Take It Apart

To multiply or divide a decimal number by a power of 10, follow these simple steps.

Step 1 **Multiplication** by a whole number *increases* the value of a number.

$0.54 \times 10,000 =$ ___

Count the number of zeros in the power of 10. There are 4 zeros in 10,000.

Step 2 Move the decimal point in the decimal number to the *right* the same number of spaces.

$0.54 \times 10,000 = 0.5400 = 5400$

Step 3 Insert commas into the product.

$0.54 \times 10,000 = 5,400$

Step 1 **Division** by a whole number *decreases* the value of a number.

$0.365 \div 10 =$ ___

Count the number of zeros in the power of 10. There is 1 zero in 10.

Step 2 Move the decimal point in the decimal number to the *left* the same number of spaces.

$0.365 \div 10 = 0.365 = .0365$

Step 3 When no digit is left of the decimal point, write a zero there.

$0.365 \div 10 = 0.0365$

Use the strategy above to answer each question.

1. $0.45 \times 1,000 =$ ___
   Does the decimal point move to the right or to the left?
   How many places?

   _____

2. $5.962 \div 100$
   Does the decimal point move to the right or to the left?
   How many places?

   _____

3. A student ticket to the school play cost $2.25. What is the cost of 10 tickets?

   _____

4. A box of 100 markers costs $189. What is the cost of 1 marker?

   _____

Put It Together

Use what you now know about multiplying and dividing decimal numbers by powers of 10 to answer each question.

1. $0.76 \times 1,000 =$ _____

2. $52.9 \div 100 =$ _____

3.   Express the product in standard form and in exponential form.

$3.84 \times 10^4 =$ ___

_____

4.   Donnie says that $0.25 \times 100 = 2,500$. Identify Donnie's mistake and show the correct answer.

_____

_____

5.   Erika has the problem $8.34 \times 1,000$. She needs to move the decimal point three places to the right There are only two digits to the right of the decimal point. What should Erika do? Explain your answer.

_____

_____

6.   Find the quotient: $0.05 \div 10^2 =$ _____

In what direction and how many places did you move the decimal point? Explain why.

_____

_____

Make It Work

Answer the questions below.

1. 3.45 ÷ 100 =

   A. 345

   B. 34.5

   C. 0.345

   D. 0.0345

2. 36,230 is the product of

   A. 36.23 × 10

   B. 36.23 × 1,000

   C. 36.23 ÷ 10

   D. 36.23 ÷ 1,000

3. The average distance between Earth and the Sun is 93,000,000 miles. How can you express this distance as a decimal number to tenths multiplied by a power of 10 in exponential form? Explain your thinking.

_____

_____

_____

4. Paul has the problem 65.04 ÷ 1,000. He adds a zero to the left of the decimal point and moves the decimal point three places to the left. Will Paul's method give the correct answer. Explain why or why not.

_____

_____

_____

_____

5. Tanya buys 300 stone pavers to make a border along a flower garden. Each one weighs 1.2 pounds. Her friend says he can use patterns in powers of 10 to mentally calculate the weight of the pavers. What method might he have used? Explain each step of your thinking.

_____

_____

_____

_____

_____

5.NBT.3.a   Read and write decimals to thousandths using base-ten numerals, number names, and expanded form, e.g., $347.392 = 3 \times 100 + 4 \times 10 + 7 \times 1 + 3 \times \left(\frac{1}{10}\right) + 9 \times \left(\frac{1}{100}\right) + 2 \times \left(\frac{1}{1000}\right)$.

Real World Connections

Key Words

decimal number

tenths place

hundredths place

thousandths place

standard form

word form

expanded form

Jamie ran a 50-meter dash in 16.38 seconds. This is a **decimal number** because it contains a decimal point and digits to the right of the decimal point. These digits have place values that are less than 1. Look at the number on a place-value chart.

← whole numbers			.	decimal places →		
100s	10s	1s	.	$\frac{1}{10}$	$\frac{1}{100}$	$\frac{1}{1,000}$
	1	6	.	3	8	

The first place to the right of the decimal is **tenths place**. Its place value is $\frac{1}{10}$ or 0.1. The next place is **hundredths place**. Its place value is $\frac{1}{100}$, or 0.01. The third place is **thousandths place**. Its place value is $\frac{1}{1,000}$, or 0.001.

To read a decimal number, say its word form.
  ◦ Read the whole number part as a whole number: *sixteen*
  ◦ For the decimal point say: *and*
  ◦ Read the decimal part as a whole number: *thirty-eight*
  ◦ Then name the place value of the last digit: *hundredths*

The number 0.38 has only a decimal part. Read it as: *thirty-eight hundredths.*

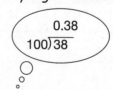

Standard form: 16.38   **Word form:** *sixteen and thirty-eight hundredths*

Another way to write Jamie's time is in expanded form. **Expanded form** shows a number as the sum of the products of the digits and their place values. Look at the products for Jamie's number.

The value of the digit 1 is (1×10).
The value of the digit 6 is (6×1).
The value of the digit 3 is $\left(3 \times \frac{1}{10}\right)$.
The value of the digit 8 is $\left(8 \times \frac{1}{100}\right)$.

Expanded form: $(1 \times 10) + (6 \times 1) + \left(3 \times \frac{1}{10}\right) + \left(8 \times \frac{1}{100}\right)$.

 ## Take It Apart

Follow these steps to read a decimal number or write a decimal number in expanded or standard form.

Read a decimal number.

Step 1 Read the number 45.903. Say *and* for the decimal point.
Look at the digits in the whole number part. There is a 4 in the tens place and a 5 in the ones place. Say the whole number: *forty-five*

Step 2 Read the decimal part as if it were a whole number: *nine hundred three*

Step 3 The last digit, 3, is in the thousandths place. Say: *thousandths*

Step 4 Read 45.903 as *forty-five and nine hundred three thousandths*.

Write a decimal number in expanded form.

Step 1 Write 18.24 in expanded form.
Identify the place value of each digit.

Step 2 Express the value of the digit as a product of the digit and its place value.

1 ten	1×10
8 ones	8×1
2 tenths	$2 \times \frac{1}{10}$
4 hundredths	$4 \times \frac{1}{100}$

Step 3 Show the number as the sum of the products of the digits and their place values.

$$(1 \times 10) + (8 \times 1) + \left(2 \times \tfrac{1}{10}\right) + \left(4 \times \tfrac{1}{100}\right)$$

Write a decimal number in standard form.

Step 1 $(2 \times 100) + (3 \times 10) + (4 \times 1) + \left(6 \times \tfrac{1}{10}\right) + \left(5 \times \tfrac{1}{100}\right) + \left(4 \times \tfrac{1}{1,000}\right)$

Simplify the expression.

$$200 + 30 + 4 + \tfrac{6}{10} + \tfrac{5}{100} + \tfrac{4}{1,000}$$

Step 2 Place the digits by place value: 234.654

Use what you know about reading and writing decimals to write these numbers.

1. Write 527.623 in expanded form.

_____

2. Write thirty-three and eighty-four hundredths in standard form. _____

Put It Together

Express each decimal number in word form. These are the words you say when you read the number.

1. 0.65 _____

2. 12.311 _____

3. 692.14 _____

Express each decimal number in standard form

4. $(8 \times 10) + (6 \times 1) + (5 \times \frac{1}{10}) + (2 \times \frac{1}{100})$ _____

5. $(9 \times 100) + (3 \times 10) + (4 \times 1) + (3 \times \frac{1}{100}) + (5 \times \frac{1}{1,000})$ _____

6. three thousand, five hundred twenty-one and seventy-one hundredths _____

7. 0.56 _____

Use what you know about reading and writing decimals to answer each question.

8. The distance from Earth to the nearest star, *Proxima Centauri*, is about four and twenty-four hundredths light years Write this distance in standard form.

_____

9. Preston read that $\frac{9}{16th}$ of an inch is 0.5625 inches. Write this decimal in expanded form. (Think: What whole number place comes before 1,000? What decimal place probably comes after $\frac{1}{1,000}$?)

_____

 Peoples Common Core Mathematics

Make It Work

Answer the questions below.

1. Write in standard form:
three hundred seventy-two and eighty hundred one thousandths

  A. 372.81

  B. 372.801

  C. 300.7281

  D. 300.072

2. Which is the word form of this number?

  10.802

  A. ten and eight hundred two thousandths

  B. one hundred eight and two thousandths

  C. ten and eighty-two hundredths

  D. one hundred and eighty-two hundredths

3. During one play, Bret's football team gained seven and four hundred seventy-eight thousandths yards. What is this distance in standard form?

_____

4. Nina rides her bicycle to her cousin's house. The distance is three and four hundred fifteen thousandths of a mile. Express the distance in expanded form.

_____

5. Write the number below in two different forms.
two thousand sixty-five and four hundred eighty-three thousandths

Standard Form: _____

Expanded Form:

_____

The three forms of the number all tell the same information. What do they tell about the number? Include an example.

_____

_____

_____

Lesson 11 Comparing Decimals to the Thousandths Place

5.NBT.3.b Compare two decimals to thousandths based on meanings of the digits in each place, using >, =, and < symbols to record the results of comparisons.

Real World Connections

Key Word

symbols

greater than (>)

less than (<)

equal to (=)

Michael made some granola. He placed it in two bags. Then he weighed the bags. The weights, in pounds, were: 0.48, and 0.475. Which bag weighs more? One way to compare the weights is to write the numbers on a place-value chart like the one below. Add a zero to 0.48, so both numbers have three decimal places. Remember, adding a zero at the end of a decimal number does not change its value.

ones	.	tenths	hundredths	thousandths
0	.	4	8	0
0	.	4	7	5

To compare the numbers, compare the digits in each place. Start with the place that has the greatest value. Then move right until you reach a place where the digits are not equal.

Compare the digits in tenths place. 4 = 4
The tenths places are equal in value.

Compare the digits in hundredths place.
8 > 7 This means that 0.480 > 0.475.
The bag with 0.48 pounds of granola weighs more.

Use **symbols** to compare the numbers:
greater than (>)
less than (<)
equal to (=)

Another way to compare decimal numbers is to write them so decimal points line up.

        0.280
        0.283
Compare the digits in each place.
Tenths place, 2 = 2   Hundredths place, 8 = 8   Thousandths place, 3 > 0

0.283 > 0.28 and 0.28 < 0.283

 Take It Apart

Follow these steps to compare two decimal numbers.

Step 1 Use the symbol $>$ to compare the value of 0.375 and 0.384.
Write the numbers so the decimal points align.

    0.375
    0.384

Step 2 Compare the digits in tenths place. $3 = 3$

Step 3 Compare the digits in hundredths place. $8 > 7$
You do not need to compare 5 and 4 because 8 hundredths is greater than 7 hundredths.

Step 4 Compare the numbers. $0.384 > 0.375$

Follow these steps to compare two numbers that have a whole number and a decimal part.

Step 1 Use the symbol $<$ to compare the value of 15.87 and 15.642.
Write the numbers so the decimal points align. Add a zero so they have the same number of decimal places.

    15.870
    15.642

Step 2 Start with the place that has the greatest value, tens place. $1 = 1$

Step 3 Move right until you reach a place where the digits are not equal.
ones place $5 = 5$
tenths place $6 < 8$
You do not need to compare any more digits because 6 tenths is less than 8 tenths.

Step 4 Compare the numbers. $15.642 < 15.87$

Use what you know about comparing decimal numbers to answer these questions.

1. Jane wrote $4.23 > 4.18$. Then she flipped the comparison and wrote $4.18 < 4.23$. Are the two comparisons true? Explain your answer in terms of place value.

    _____

2. Use the numbers 6.297 and 6.792 to write two comparisons.

    _____

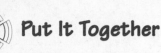

Put It Together

Use the symbol >, =, or < to make each comparison below.

1. 0.832 _____ 0.38

2. 2.47 _____ 2.474

3. 5.008 _____ 5.02

4. 0.452 _____ 0.45

Use the information below to answer questions 5–7.

There are three puppies in a litter. At age six weeks their weights in kilograms are:

Puppy 1   Puppy 2   Puppy 3
1.93 kg   1.95 kg   1.096 kg

5. Which puppy weighs the most?

_____

6. Which puppy weighs the least?

_____

7. Use the symbol > to compare the three weights. Start with the greatest weight.

_____

8. Vanessa needs to decide which number is greater, 8.43×10^3 or 8.87×10^3. She's not sure what to do. Write a sentence or two that will help her understand the problem.

_____

_____

9. Elton has two boxes of baseball cards. One box weighs 1.68 pounds. The other weighs 1.6 pounds. He moves some cards from the heavier box to the lighter box. Now their weights are equal. Write a comparison that shows the weights of the two boxes after he moves some cards.

_____

Make It Work

Answer the questions below.

1. Which number makes the statement
   ___ > 34.16 true?

   A. 3.516

   B. 3.518

   C. 34.21

   D. 34.06

2. Which comparison is true?

   A. 0.53 = 0.530

   B. 0.024 > 0.04

   C. 0.72 < 0.693

   D. 0.87 < 0.807

3. The coach uses a stopwatch to time a race. The times for the first three runners to finish are: 54.3 seconds, 54.401 seconds, and 54.034 seconds. Which is the time for the first place winner? (Remember, the winner will take the least amount of time.) Show how you found your answer.

   _____

   _____

4. Last softball season, Julian had a batting average of 0.277. Omar's batting average was 0.259. Who had the higher batting average?

   _____

   Write a sentence that includes a comparison symbol to support your answer.

   _____

5. Dara completed an obstacle course in 26.38 seconds. Tiffyn completed the same course in 26.023 seconds. Ron's time was faster than Dara's but slower than Tiffyn's.

   ∘ Write a time that could be Ron's time. Show your work.

   _____

   ∘ Write a comparison of the three times. Place the fastest time on the left in your comparison.

   _____

5.NBT.4   Use place value understanding to round decimals to any place.

Real World Connections

Toolbox

calculator

place-value chart

Key Words

round

number line

Jamal bought a notebook that cost $5.89. The tax rate is 8.25%. To find the tax, he used the percent key on his calculator. The result was 0.485925. The store receipt shows $0.49 in tax. What explains the difference?

Our money system goes to hundredths (cents). The cash register in a store was programmed to round the tax to the nearest cent, or to the hundredths place. When you round to the hundredths place there are only two digits to the right of the decimal point.

When you **round** a number, you find an estimate of the number to a given place value. How do you round a decimal number? Use the same rules you use for rounding whole numbers.

- Underline the digit in the place to which you want to round. In this case, the hundredths place.

  0.4<u>8</u>5925

- Look at the digit in the place to its right. In this case, the thousandths place.

  0.4<u>8</u>**5**925

- If the digit to the right is *less than* 5, do not change the underlined digit. If the digit to the right is 5 *or more*, add 1 to the underlined digit.

- The digit to the right of 8 is 5. Add 1 to 8.
  Omit the digits with a place value less than hundredths.

  0.485925 rounded to the nearest hundredth is 0.49

On a **number line,** every point represents a number. A number line can help you understand the rules for rounding. Round 1.22 to the nearest tenth.

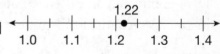

1.22 is between 1.2 and 1.3.
It is less than 1.25 so it is closer to 1.2.
1.22 rounded to the nearest tenth is 1.2.

        Peoples Common Core Mathematics

Take It Apart

Use what you know about rounding decimal numbers to answer the question.

Ms. Day looks at her utility bill. She used 1,008 kilowatt (kW) hours of electricity. The cost of the electricity is $0.03653 per kW hours. She calculates the charge as $36.82224. What is the charge rounded to the nearest hundredth?

Step 1 Underline the digit in the hundredths place.

36.8<u>2</u>224

Step 2 Look at the digit in the place to its right. The digit is 2.

36.8<u>2</u>224

Step 3 The digit 2 is less than 5.

Do not change the digit in the hundredths place.

Omit all digits with a lesser place value.
$36.82224 rounded to the nearest hundredth is $36.82.

You also can use a place-value chart to round numbers.
Round 8.056 to the nearest tenth.

Step 1 Write the number on a place-value chart.
Look at the digit in the tenths place, 0.

Ones		Tenths	Hundredths	Thousandths
8	·	0	5	6

Step 2 Look at the digit to its right, 5.

Step 3 The digit 5 is equal to 5 or more.
　　　　Add 1 to the digit in the tenths place.
　　　　0 + 1 = 1

　　　　8.056 rounded to the nearest tenth is 8.1.

Use the steps above to round 0.5628

1. to the nearest tenth _____

2. to the nearest hundredth _____

3. to the nearest thousandth _____

Put It Together

Use what you know about place value and rounding to round the following numbers. Follow the rules you learned, even if the situation is different from the ones you have seen.

Round each number to the nearest tenth.

1. 0.4592   **2.** 0.5376   **3.** 18.0645

_____   _____   _____

Round each number to the nearest hundredth.

4. 0.0573   **5.** 0.9462   **6.** 12.0073

_____   _____   _____

Round each number to the nearest thousandth.

7. 0.0235   **8.** 1.3691   **9.** 8.8307

_____   _____   _____

Use place value to answer each question below. Work with a classmate if you would like.

10. Frank rounded 0.3043 to the nearest hundredth and got 0.30. Explain why the answer is 0.30, not 0.3.

_____

_____

11. Gina needs to round 12.9726 to the nearest tenth. She looks at the digits but isn't sure what to do. Round the number and explain your thinking.

_____

_____

Make It Work

Answer the questions below.

1. Round $0.51948 to the nearest hundredth.

   A. $0.51

   B. $0.52

   C. $0.59

   D. $0.60

2. Victor rounded 4.7809 to 4.781. He rounded to the

   A. tenths place

   B. hundredths place

   C. thousandths place

   D. ten thousandths place

3. Sid rounded the two numbers below to the same place.
    174.9652 to 174.97
    68.8993 to 68.90
If he rounds 6.3801 to the same place what will the rounded number be? How do you know?

_____

_____

4. Maria scored 9.657 on her gymnastics routine. Stella scored 9.725 on hers. Are both girls likely to be happy if the scores are rounded to the nearest tenth? Explain your answer.

_____

_____

5. An activity says, "Write four numbers that when rounded to the hundredths place are 0.45." A student wrote the four numbers below.

0.4509   0.4538   0.4438   0.4495

Are the numbers correct? Explain why or why not.

_____

_____

_____

5.NBT.5 Fluently multiply multi-digit whole numbers using the standard algorithm.

Real World Connections

Toolbox

calculator

Key Words

factors

product

partial product

Sal owns a pizza shop. He orders 212 cases of tomato sauce. Each case contains 24 cans of tomato sauce. How many cans of tomato sauce are in the order? Multiply to find the answer: 212 cases × 24 cans per case. The two numbers you multiply are called **factors.** The answer is called the **product.**

Sal knows that 212 = 200 + 10 + 2. He also knows how to multiply by 10s. He says he can multiply 212 × 24 mentally.

○ Sal multiplies by 4 ones.
$$4 \times 212 = 848$$

○ Then by 2 tens.
$$212 \times 20 =$$
$$(212 \times 10) \times 2 =$$
$$2{,}120 \times 2 = 4{,}240$$

○ He adds the two *partial products.*
$$848 + 4{,}240 = 5{,}088$$

A **partial product** is the result of multiplying *one factor* by only *one digit of the second factor*. Sal multiplied *one factor* (212) by *one digit of the second factor* (2). Then he multiplied by the other digit in the second factor (4).

Sal's method works for his problem because the numbers are easy to work with. Here is another way to do the same multiplication. This method will work for numbers that are more difficult or impossible to multiply mentally.

○ Multiply 212 by 4 ones.

○ Write a placeholder zero in ones place. Then multiply 24 by 2 tens.

○ Add the partial products.

```
  212
× 24   ← 4 ones × 212
  848   ← partial product
```

```
   212
 × 24   ← 2 tens × 212
   848
  4240   ← partial product
```

```
   212
 × 24
   848   ← partial product
  4240   ← partial product
  5,088  ← product
```

You can reverse the order of the numbers in multiplication and the product will be the same:

$$212 \times 24 = 24 \times 212.$$

Copying is illegal.

Take It Apart

Use these steps to multiply a three-digit number by a two-digit number.

Step 1 Multiply by the ones to find the first partial product.

$4 \times 3 = 12$ Regroup.

$5 \times 3 = 15 + 1 = 16$ Regroup.

$7 \times 3 = 21 + 1 = 22$

$$
\begin{array}{r}
{\scriptstyle 1\ 1} \\
\mathbf{754} \\
\times\ \mathbf{23} \\
\hline
2262
\end{array}
$$
← partial product

Step 2 Write a placeholder zero in ones place. Multiply by the tens to find the second partial product.

$4 \times 2 = 8$

$5 \times 2 = 10$ Regroup.

$7 \times 2 = 14 + 1 = 15$

$$
\begin{array}{r}
{\scriptstyle 1} \\
{\scriptstyle 1\ 1} \\
\mathbf{754} \\
\times\ \mathbf{23} \\
\hline
2262 \\
15080
\end{array}
$$
← partial product

$$
\begin{array}{r}
754 \\
\times\ 23 \\
\hline
2262 \\
+15080 \\
\hline
17{,}342
\end{array}
$$
← product

Step 3 Add the partial products.

You can use the method above to multiply three-digit numbers.

- The factor 128 is a three-digit number, so there are three partial products.

- The first multiplication, 623×8, requires regrouping.

- Notice the pattern of placeholder zeros in the partial products.

$$
\begin{array}{r}
{\scriptstyle 1\ 2} \\
623 \\
\times\ 128 \\
\hline
4984 \\
12460 \\
+\ 62300 \\
\hline
79{,}744
\end{array}
$$
← 8 ones × 623
← 2 tens × 623
← 1 hundred × 623

Use the steps above to find each product. If it's helpful, use grid paper to keep your columns straight. Use a calculator to check your answers. Divide the final product by one of the factors. The quotient should be the other factor.

1. $\begin{array}{r} 821 \\ \times\ 42 \\ \hline \end{array}$
2. $\begin{array}{r} 503 \\ \times\ 66 \\ \hline \end{array}$
3. $\begin{array}{r} 748 \\ \times\ 35 \\ \hline \end{array}$
4. $\begin{array}{r} 692 \\ \times\ 278 \\ \hline \end{array}$

Put It Together

Use what you now know about multiplying whole numbers to find each product.

1. 732
    × 13

2. 420
    × 52

3. 396
    × 80

4. 304
    × 64

5. 562
    × 47

6. 683
    × 209

7. 274
    × 858

8. 503
    × 466

9. 321
    × 239

Answer the questions. Share your ideas with a classmate.

10. Which multiplication above might be easier if the factors are reversed? Explain your choice.

_____

_____

11. You know you can use division to check multiplication. Explain how you could use multiplication to check multiplication. Use a simple example.

_____

_____

12. A store is having a sale on HD televisions. They sell 115 televisions at an average price of $328. What is the dollar amount of the total sales? Show your work. Remember to set up your problem in a way that makes the multiplication easier.

_____

_____

Make It Work

Answer the questions below.

1. Find the product.

853
× 27

A. 7,677

B. 7,748

C. 22,292

D. 23,031

2. Find the product.

217
× 485

A. 3,698

B. 11,501

C. 105,245

D. 886,445

3. Rajeev used a zero as a placeholder in this problem on the right. Explain its purpose.

_____

_____

35
× 12
70
35**0**

4. Anita did the multiplication on the right. The answer seems too large. She thinks something is wrong, but she isn't sure what. Identify where Anita made an error and correct her mistake.

_____

_____

465
× 208
3720
000
+ 930000

5. The flight distance between Miami, Florida, and Buenos Aires, Argentina is about 4,364 miles. One businessman estimates that he has made this flight 28 times.

○ How many miles has he flown on these trips? Show your work.

_____

○ Describe a way to check your answer.

_____

_____

5.NBT.6 Find whole-number quotients of whole numbers with up to four-digit dividends and two-digit divisors, using strategies based on place value, the properties of operations, and/or the relationship between multiplication and division. Illustrate and explain the calculation by using equations, rectangular arrays, and/or area models.

Real World Connections

Toolbox

calculator

Key Words

dividend

divisor

Barbara buys different types of birdseeds in large quantities. Then she mixes them into her own special blend—Barbara's Best for Birds. Barbara mixes up 768 pounds of seeds and packages them into 16-pound bags. How many bags will she have?

Barbara shares out the seeds into groups of 16 pounds. This is a division problem. The **dividend** is the number divided—768. The **divisor** is the number divided into the dividend—16. Just as multiplication is repeated addition, division is repeated subtraction. You could subtract the 16 from 768 over and over, but this would take a long time, and it would be easy to make a subtraction error.

A more efficient method is the same one you use to divide with a 1-digit divisor. This method is a series of smaller divisions, as shown below.

$$
\begin{array}{r}
48 \\
16{\overline{\smash{)}768}} \\
-64{\downarrow} \\
\hline
128 \\
-128 \\
\hline
0
\end{array}
$$

◦ 16 > 7, divide 16 into 76.

◦ The *first division* is 76 ÷ 16. Look closely at the place values. What you are really dividing is 760 ÷ 16 = 40, remainder 12. But don't write the zero.
76 ÷ 16 = 4, remainder 12.

◦ For the *second division*, bring down the 8. Then divide again.
128 ÷ 16 = 8, remainder 0.

Here are some tips about dividing.

◦ If necessary, use grid paper to keep your columns straight.

◦ Treat zeros as you would any other digit. If you don't know what to do with a zero, ask yourself, "What would I do if the zero were a 1?" You will almost always do the same thing with the zero.

◦ Division is much easier using your knowledge of multiplication facts. You could also use a chart or a calculator as an aid.

◦ Use a calculator to check your answer. Division and multiplication are opposites. Multiply the divisor and the quotient, you should get the dividend. If you don't, review the steps in the division.

 ## Take It Apart

Use these steps to divide a four-digit dividend by a two-digit divisor. In each smaller division, use the steps: *Divide, Multiply, Subtract, Bring Down.*

Step 1   First division.
Divide: 32 > 4. 46 ÷ 32 = __.
     Think: 32 × 2 = 64. 64 > 46. Try 1.
Multiply: 32 × 1 = 32
Subtract: 46 − 32 = 14
Bring Down: Bring down the 7.

```
      1
32)4672
  − 32↓
    147
```

Step 2   Second division.
Divide: 147 ÷ 32 = __.
     Think: 30 × 5 = 150. 150 > 147. Try 4.
Multiply: 32 × 4 = 128
Subtract: 147 − 128 = 19
Bring Down: Bring down the 2.

```
     14
32)4672
  − 32
   147
  − 128↓
    192
```

Step 3   Third division.
Divide: 192 ÷ 32 = __.
     Think: 30 × 7 = 210. 210 > 192. Try 6.
Multiply: 32 × 6 = 192
Subtract: 192 − 192 = 0

```
    146
32)4672
  − 32
   147
  −128
   192
  −192
     0
```

Use the steps above to find each quotient. You may use a separate sheet of paper to work out the problems, as shown in the examples above.

1. 1,624 ÷ 58 _____

2. 7,208 ÷ 34 _____

3. 4,896 ÷ 48 _____

4. 6,264 ÷ 87 _____

Put It Together

Use what you now know about multiplying whole numbers to find each product.

1. 4,056 ÷ 52

_____

2. 5,934 ÷ 46

_____

3. 3,283 ÷ 67

_____

4. 3,066 ÷ 21

_____

5. 7,164 ÷ 12

_____

6. 1,296 ÷ 72

_____

7. 5,681 ÷ 23

_____

8. 10,881 ÷ 27

_____

9. 4,905 ÷ 327

_____

Answer the questions. Share your ideas with a classmate.

10. Huong and her family drive from Seattle, Washington, to Miami, Florida. The distance is about 3,300 miles. If their average speed is 55 miles per hour, what is the driving time? Show your work.

_____

_____

11. Two students will work together to divide 29,430 ÷ 30. One student says it will be hard because of the zeros. The other student says the zeros make it easy. Find the quotient. Then tell which student you agree with, and explain why.

_____

_____

12. Matt has the division 125 ÷ 5 = 25. He says he can check his answer by dividing 125 ÷ 25. The quotient should be 5. Is Matt correct? Explain why or why not.

_____

_____

Make It Work

Answer the questions below.

1. Find the quotient.
1,596 ÷ 38

  A. 42   **B.** 43

  C. 53   **D.** 55

2. Find the quotient.
1,065 ÷ 15

  A. 43   **B.** 68

  C. 71   **D.** 139

3. Winton divided 4,509 by 9 and got 51. Is his answer correct? If not, what mistake did he likely make? Show your work.

_____

_____

4. In multiplication, the order of the factors does not matter: $3 \times 4 = 4 \times 3$. In division, the order of the dividend and the divisor does matter: $125 \div 25 \neq 25 \div 125$. Explain why this is true.

_____

_____

5. Ming discovers another way to divide 864 by 27, as shown on the right below.

○ She writes 864 in expanded form: $800 + 60 + 4$.   ○ Then she finds how many groups of 27 are in each part.   ○ She subtracts. Each time there is a little left over.   ○ She finds the sum of the three divisions and the division of the leftovers. She says it is the quotient.

$$\begin{array}{r} \mathbf{29 + \ 2 + 0} \\ 27\overline{)800 + 60 + 4} \\ \underline{-783 \ -54 \ -0} \\ 17 + \ 6 + 4 = 27 \qquad 27\overline{)27}^{\,1} \end{array}$$

Quotient: $29 + 2 + 0 + 1 = 32$

Why does Ming have to divide the sum of the leftovers by 27 and include it in the quotient?

_____

_____

Do you think Ming's method is an easier or a more difficult method? Explain your answer.

_____

Lesson 15 Using Properties of Operations to Divide Whole Numbers

5.NBT.6 Find whole-number quotients of whole numbers with up to four-digit dividends and two-digit divisors, using strategies based on place value, the properties of operations, and/or the relationship between multiplication and division. Illustrate and explain the calculation by using equations, rectangular arrays, and/or area models.

Real World Connections

Terrance knows that division and multiplication are **inverse operations,** or operations that "undo" each other. He also understands the **distributive property,** which says: *A factor times the sum of two addends is equal to the sum of the products of the addends when they are multiplied separately:* $2 \times (3 + 4) = (2 \times 3) + (2 \times 4)$. What he does not understand is how they are related to division. His cousin shows him a model that might help him out.

Inverse operations: $84 \div 6 =$ __, $6 \times$ __ $= 84$. The division asks, "How many groups of 6 are in 84?" Find out by answering the question, "How many groups of 6 make 84?"

Use a model with 6 rows and make groups of six.

- First, take 10 sixes, as shown on the model.

- Subtract to find the remainder:

    $84 - 60 = 24$

- Then take 4 sixes, as shown on the model.

- Subtract to find the remainder:

    $24 - 24 = 0$

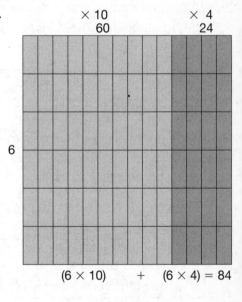

(6×10) $+$ $(6 \times 4) = 84$

Now you know that $(6 \times 10) + (6 \times 4) = 84$. Apply the Distributive Property and simplify.

$6 \times (10 + 4) = 84$
$\quad 6 \times \underline{14} = 84$

The unknown factor and quotient are both 14. Look at the division on the right. It also takes out groups of 6.

$$
\begin{array}{r}
4 \\
10 \\
6\overline{)84} \\
-60 \times \underline{10} \quad \text{Take out 10 groups of 6.} \\
24 \\
-24 \times \underline{4} \quad \text{Take out 4 groups of 6.} \\
0
\end{array}
$$

Take It Apart

Use inverse operations and the distributive property to find the quotient. As divisors and dividends increase in size, using a model can help to represent areas. Keep in mind that models are not exactly proportional.

Step 1 $1,560 \div 13 = $ ___

- Write the inverse operation:
  $13 \times $ ___ $= 1,560$
- Take out 100 groups of 13, or 1,300.
- Subtract to find the remainder:
  $1,560 - 1,300 = 260$

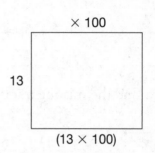

$\times 100$

13

(13×100)

Step 2
- Take out 20 groups of 13, or 260.
- Subtract to find the remainder:
  $260 - 260 = 0$

(Taking out 20 groups of 13 is the same as taking out 10 groups of 13 twice.)

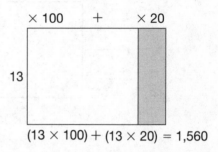

$\times 100 \quad + \quad \times 20$

13

$(13 \times 100) + (13 \times 20) = 1,560$

Step 3 Write an equation to represent the multiplication.

$(13 \times 100) + (13 \times 20) = 1,560$

Step 4 Apply the Distributive Property to find the quotient. The missing product and quotient are 120.

$13 \times (100 + 20) = 1,560$
$13 \times \underline{120} = 1,560$

Use the steps above to find the quotient. The model is shown, but not labeled.

1. $1,944 \div 18 = $ _____

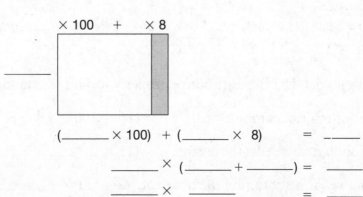

$\times 100 \quad + \quad \times 8$

$(\underline{\hspace{1cm}} \times 100) + (\underline{\hspace{1cm}} \times 8) \quad = \underline{\hspace{1cm}}$

$\underline{\hspace{1cm}} \times (\underline{\hspace{1cm}} + \underline{\hspace{1cm}}) = \underline{\hspace{1cm}}$

$\underline{\hspace{1cm}} \times \underline{\hspace{1cm}} \quad = \underline{\hspace{1cm}}$

Put It Together

Use what you now know about finding quotients using inverse operations and the distributive property to answer the questions.

Write the inverse operation for each division problem.

1. $648 \div 36 =$ _____ $36 \times$ _____ $= 648$

2. $2{,}967 \div 23 =$ _____ $23 \times$ _____ $= 2{,}967$

3. Use the model to find the missing quotient. The model is shown but not labeled.

   $1{,}320 \div 11 =$ _____

   $\times 100 \quad + \quad \times$ _____

   (_____ $\times 100$) + (_____ $\times$ _____) = _____

   _____ $\times$ (_____ + _____) = _____

   _____ $\times$ _____ = _____

4. Reva made this model. Fill in the blanks to help her relate it to the long division method.

   $11 \times$ _____ $= 1{,}243$
   $\times 100 + \times 10 + \times 3$

   11

   $(11 \times 100) + (11 \times 10) + (11 \times 3)$

   $\left. \begin{array}{r} 3 \\ 10 \\ 100 \end{array} \right\} 113$

   $11{\overline{\smash{\big)}\,1{,}243}}$
   $\underline{-1{,}100} \times 100$ Take out _____ groups of _____.
   143
   $\underline{-110} \times 10$ Take out _____ groups of _____.
   33
   $\underline{-33} \times 3$ Take out _____ groups of _____.
   0

5. Look back at Reva's model. Use the distributive property to find the quotient.

   ○ Circle two groups Reva can combine first. (11×100) (11×10) (11×3)

   ○ Write an equation that represents the answer. $(11 \times$ _____ $) + (11 \times$ _____ $) =$ _____

   ○ Use the Distributive Property to find the quotient. $11 \times ($ _____ $+$ _____ $) =$ _____

   $11 \times$ _____ $=$ _____

Make It Work

Answer the questions below.

1. Which is the inverse operation of
   2,376 ÷ 18 = ___?

   A. 2,376 × 18 = ____

   B. 18 × ___ = 2,376

   C. 18 ÷ ___ = 2,376

   D. 18 × 2,376 = ____

2. Which could be the first step in this division?
   62)‾1‾,‾1‾1‾6‾

   A. Take out 10 groups of 62.

   B. Take out 100 groups of 62.

   C. Take out 62 groups of 10.

   D. Take out 62 groups of 100.

3. Dennis has this problem: 240 ÷ 2. He has this equation: (2 × 100) + (2 × 20) = 240
   Show how he can use this information to find the quotient.

   _____

   _____

4. Laurie has this information: (65 × 10) + (65 × 8) = 1,170. Use it to write a division statement.

   _____

5. Find the quotient. 375 ÷ 15

   Use inverse operations and the distributive property. | Use long division.

   If you do not get the same quotient, use your calculator to find the quotient. Review your work
   and circle your mistake in thinking.

   _____

5.NBT.6 Find whole-number quotients of whole numbers with up to four-digit dividends and two-digit divisors, using strategies based on place value, the properties of operations, and/or the relationship between multiplication and division. Illustrate and explain the calculation by using equations, rectangular arrays, and/or area models.

Real World Connections

Allegra is working on a math project. Her project will show how division is related to multiplication. She will include factor triangles like the one below. Her classmates can use each triangle to write related division and multiplication facts. The related facts all belong to the same **fact family.** They show that division and multiplication are **inverse operations,** or operations that undo each other.

$$6 \times 8 = 48 \qquad 48 \div 8 = 6$$
$$8 \times 6 = 48 \qquad 48 \div 6 = 8$$

Allegra also could use an array to show the relationship between three numbers in a fact family—4, 9, and 36.

$$4 \times 9 = 36 \qquad 9 \times 4 = 3($$

$$36 \div 9 = 4 \qquad 36 \div 4 = 9$$

Then she can show how this fact family is helpful when dividing $382 \div 42$ using long division.

Ask: How many groups of 42 are in 382?

Think: $38 \div 4 = ?$
$\quad 4 \times 9 = 36$
$\quad 4 \times 10 = 40$

$40 > 38$. Try 9.
Nine is correct.

$$42\overline{)382}$$

$$\begin{array}{r} 9 \\ 42\overline{)382} \\ -378 \\ \hline 4 \end{array}$$

Allegra actually used multiplication facts to estimate the first **partial quotient.** She knows that 4 will go into 38 between 9 and 10 times. She multiplies by 9 and finds the remainder.

Take It Apart

Identify the multiplication facts that can help with the long division.

Step 1	Find the first partial quotient: 345 ÷ 72	$72\overline{)3{,}456}$ □	$72\overline{)3{,}456}$ 4
	Ask: How many groups of 72 are in 345?		−2 88
			57
	Think: 7 × __ is closest to 34?		
	$\qquad$ 7 × 4 = 28		
	$\qquad$ 7 × 5 = 35		
	35 > 34, try 4.		
Step 2	Find the second partial quotient: 576 ÷ 72	$72\overline{)3{,}456}$ 4□	$72\overline{)3{,}456}$ 48
	Ask: How many groups of 72 are in 576?	−2 88↓	−2 88
		576	576
	Think: 7 × __ is closest to 57?		−576
	$\qquad$ 7 × 8 = 56		0
	$\qquad$ 7 × 9 = 72		
	72 > 57, try 8.		
Step 3	The multiplication facts that can help with this division are: 7 × 4 = 28 and 7 × 8 = 56.		

Use the steps above to find two multiplication facts that will help with each division.

1. $36\overline{)2{,}988}$

    Fact: _____

    Fact: _____

2. $68\overline{)3{,}196}$

    Fact: _____

    Fact: _____

Put It Together

Use what you now know about the relationship between multiplication and division to answer each question.

1. Explain the meaning of the statement below. Include an example in your explanation.

   Division is the inverse operation of multiplication.

   _____

   _____

There are three numbers in a fact family. Identify the missing number for each fact family below.

2. 22, _____, 220   3. _____, 12, 216   4. 4, 28, _____

Use long division to find each quotient. What multiplication facts can help with each division below?

5. 18)‾504‾

   _____

   Fact: _____

   Fact: _____

6. 58)‾1,566‾

   _____

   Fact: _____

   Fact: _____

7. 46)‾3,312‾

   _____

   Fact: _____

   Fact: _____

   _____

   _____

8. How can you use multiplication to check each quotient in questions 5–7? Explain why your method will work.

   _____

   _____

Make It Work

Answer the questions below.

1. Which is the third number for a fact family?
   5, 45, ___

   A. 6

   B. 9

   C. 40

   D. 50

2. Which fact is in the same fact family
   as $7 \times 6 = 42$?

   A. $2 \times 21 = 42$

   B. $3 \times 14 = 42$

   C. $42 \div 2 = 12$

   D. $42 \div 6 = 7$

3. Jonah drew this area model. Use the relationship between multiplication and division to find the missing factor. Show your work.

$\times$ ___	
16	480

_____

4. A student finds this quotient: $448 \div 32 = 14$. He says he can check it by dividing $32 \div 448$. Is the student correct? Explain your answer.

_____

5. Kurt reads this statement in his math book.

   If you know your multiplication facts, you can use them to estimate quotients.

   ○ Explain what the statement means.

   _____

   _____

   ○ He has the problem $438 \div 6$. How can he apply the statement to estimate $43 \div 6$?

   _____

   _____

5.NBT.7 Add, subtract, multiply, and divide decimals to hundredths, using concrete models or drawings and strategies based on place value, properties of operations, and/or the relationship between addition and subtraction; relate the strategy to a written method and explain the reasoning used.

Real World Connections

Toolbox

colored pencils
2 colors

blank hundred
    squares

Ebony's supermarket has a code for every type of fruit and vegetable. You place an item on the computerized scale. Then you enter the code. The scale prints out a label with the weight and cost. Ebony buys 2.3 pounds of grapes and 1.64 pounds of peaches. How many pounds of fruit is this?

To find the sum add the decimal numbers 2.3 and 1.64. Adding decimal numbers is a lot like adding whole numbers.

Look at the addition on a place value chart.

ones	.	tenths	hundredths
2	.	3	0
+1	.	6	4
3	.	**9**	4

- 2.3 has one decimal place. Remember, adding a zero to the right doesn't change the decimal's value.
- 1.64 has two decimal places.

Ebony bought 3.94 pounds of fruit.

You can use hundred squares to model the addition. The value of each hundred square is $\frac{100}{100}$, or 1. The value of each column is 0.1. The value of each small square is 0.01.

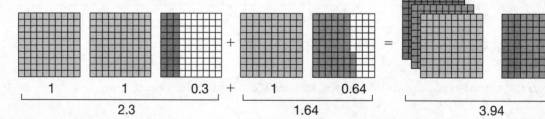

One of the peaches weighs 0.58 pound. Ebony packs it in her lunch. How many pounds of peaches are left? Subtract 1.64 − 0.58. Align the decimal points. Then subtract as if they were whole numbers. There are 1.06 pounds of peaches left.

ones	.	tenths	hundredths
1	.	6	4
−0	.	5	8
1	.	**0**	6

You can use hundred squares to model the subtraction. Show 1.64. Then mark out 0.58, or 5 tenths and 8 hundredths.

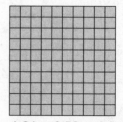 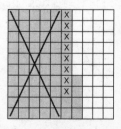

1.64 − 0.58 = 1.6

Take It Apart

To add or subtract decimal numbers, follow these steps. Remember, *always* line up the decimal points. Then add or subtract as if the numbers were whole numbers.

Add Decimal Numbers	**Subtract Decimal Numbers**

Step 1 Write the numbers. Line up the decimal points.

$$\begin{array}{r} 2.65 \\ + 4.08 \\ \hline \end{array}$$

Step 1 Write the numbers. Line up the decimal points. Add zero as a placeholder.

$$\begin{array}{r} 9.30 \\ - 5.07 \\ \hline \end{array}$$

Step 2 Add the hundredths. Regroup.

$$\begin{array}{r} {}^{1} \\ 2.65 \\ + 4.08 \\ \hline 3 \end{array}$$

Step 2 Subtract the hundredths. Regroup.

$$\begin{array}{r} {}^{210} \\ 9.\cancel{3}\cancel{0} \\ -5.07 \\ \hline 3 \end{array}$$

Step 3 Add the tenths. Bring down the decimal point.

$$\begin{array}{r} {}^{1} \\ 2.65 \\ + 4.08 \\ \hline .73 \end{array}$$

Step 3 Subtract the tenths. Bring down the decimal point.

$$\begin{array}{r} {}^{210} \\ 9.\cancel{3}\cancel{0} \\ -5.07 \\ \hline .23 \end{array}$$

Step 4 Add the ones.

$$\begin{array}{r} 2.65 \\ + 4.08 \\ \hline 6.73 \end{array}$$

Step 4 Subtract the ones.

$$\begin{array}{r} 9.30 \\ - 5.07 \\ \hline 4.23 \end{array}$$

Use the steps above to find each sum or difference.

1. $2.08 + 4.19$ 2. $3.7 + 0.35$ 3. $3.68 - 1.52$ 4. $5.07 - 3.2$

_____   _____   _____   _____

Lesson 17 **Adding and Subtracting Decimals to the Hundredths Place**

Put It Together

Use what you know about adding and subtracting decimals to find each sum or difference.

1. 0.42
    + 0.37

2. 1.58
    + 0.31

3. 0.05
    + 2.4

4. 5.67
    − 0.21

5. 0.94
    − 0.76

6. 3.02
    − 1.45

7. 1.09 + 0.85

    _____

8. 5.3 + 3.684

    _____

9. 3.042 + 0.65 + 2.738

    _____

10. 4.73 − 0.61

    _____

11. 2.34 − 0.5

    _____

12. 0.58 − 0.013

    _____

Shade the hundred squares to show 1.6 + 0.53. Use a different color for each number.

13. 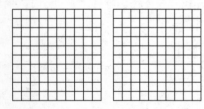 + 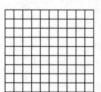 =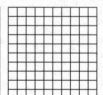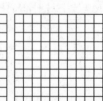

    _____ + _____ = _____

Shade the model to show 2.09 − 1.38. Place Xs on the amount subtracted.

14. 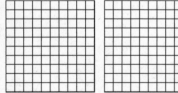 − 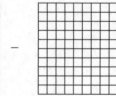 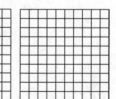 =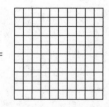

    _____ − _____ = _____

     Peoples Common Core Mathematics

Make It Work

Answer the questions below.

1. 1.07 + 2.56 =

    A. 3.26

    B. 3.36

    C. 3.53

    D. 3.63

2. 3.45 − 0.2 =

    A. 3.25

    B. 3.43

    C. 3.47

    D. 3.65

3. Write a decimal addition or subtraction sentence that means the same thing as the operation modeled on the right.

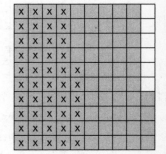

_____

4. Malcolm writes this addition problem to find a decimal sum. Can he find the correct sum using his problem? Why or why not? If necessary, rewrite the problem. You do not need to find the sum.

_____

_____

$$\begin{array}{r} 1.03 \\ 0.5 \\ + 4.2 \\ \hline \end{array}$$

5. In Terry's town, the average monthly rainfall in May is 5.79 inches. This May, he records these rainfall figures, in inches: 1.04, 2.36, 0.29, and 0.5.

Is the monthly rainfall for this May above or below average? Show your work.

_____

_____

How much above or below average is it? Show your work.

_____

_____

Lesson 18 · Multiplying and Dividing Decimals to the Hundredths Place

5.NBT.7 Add, subtract, multiply, and divide decimals to hundredths, using concrete models or drawings and strategies based on place value, properties of operations, and/or the relationship between addition and subtraction; relate the strategy to a written method and explain the reasoning used.

Real World Connections

Toolbox

colored pencils,
3 colors

Devora does not understand why 0.5 × 0.8 ≠ 40. Her sister makes the model below to show her why.

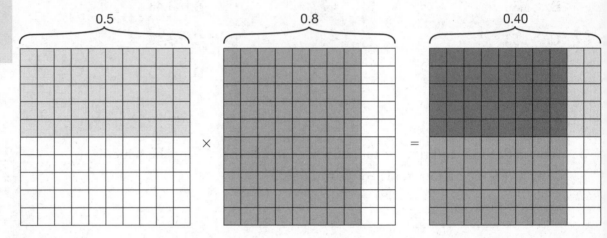

The top five rows are shaded to represent the factor 0.5. The first eight columns are shaded to represent the factor 0.8. The area where the shading overlaps shows the product. This area covers 40 small squares. The product is the decimal number 0.4. The model helped Devora understand why 40 is not a reasonable answer.

Another Way Multiply as for whole numbers. Count the total number of decimal places in the factors. Place the same number of decimal places in the product.

$$0.5 \leftarrow 1 \text{ decimal place}$$
$$\times 0.8 \leftarrow 1 \text{ decimal place}$$
$$\overline{0.40} \leftarrow 2 \text{ decimal places}$$

Remember, 0.40 = 0.4

Devora knows that multiplication and division undo each other.

If 0.5 × 0.8 = 0.4, then 0.4 ÷ 0.5 = 0.8.

$$
\begin{array}{r}
0.8 \\
5\overline{)4.0} \\
-0 \\
\hline
40 \\
-40 \\
\hline
0
\end{array}
$$

○ Before she can divide, she needs to change 0.5 to a whole number. Multiply 0.5 by a factor of 10.　　　　0.5 × 10 = 5.0

Multiply the dividend by 10 also.　　　0.4 × 10 = 4.0

○ Add a zero to the right of 4. This does not change the value of the number.

Remember: To multiply by 10, move the decimal point 1 place to the right. To multiply by 100, move it 2 places to the right.

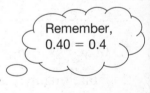

Take It Apart

To multiply or divide decimal numbers, follow these steps.

Multiply Decimal Numbers	
Step 1	**Step 2**
0.43 × 2.8 = _____ Multiply as if the numbers were whole numbers. Regroup if necessary. You do NOT need to line up the decimal points.	Count the total number of decimal places in the factors. Use this number of decimal places in the product.

Step 1:
$$\begin{array}{r} {}^{2} \\ 0.43 \\ \times\,2.8 \\ \hline 344 \\ +\,860 \\ \hline 1204 \end{array}$$

Step 2:
$$\begin{array}{r} {}^{2} \\ 0.4\,3 \leftarrow 2 \text{ decimal places} \\ \times\,2.8 \leftarrow 1 \text{ decimal place} \\ \hline 344 \\ +\,860 \\ \hline 1.204 \leftarrow 3 \text{ decimal places} \end{array}$$

Divide Decimal Numbers	
Step 1	**Step 2**
1.44 ÷ 0.6. Change 0.6 to a whole number. Move the decimal point one place to the right in the divisor and the dividend. Bring the decimal point straight up.	Divide.

Step 1:
$$0.6\overline{)1.44}$$

Step 2:
$$\begin{array}{r} 2.4 \\ 6\overline{)14.4} \\ -12\downarrow \\ \hline 24 \\ -24 \\ \hline 0 \end{array}$$

Use the steps above to find each product or quotient. Remember, the order of the factors does not matter in multiplication. You may use a separate sheet of paper to work out the problems.

1. 0.03 × 16   2. 5.7 × 0.06   3. 0.24 ÷ 0.8   4. 19.5 ÷ 1.3

_____   _____   _____   _____

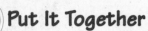 **Put It Together**

Use what you know about multiplying and dividing decimals to find each product or quotient.

1.   0.38
      × 0.75

2.   7.6
      × 0.8

3.   15.6
      × 0.35

4. 0.3)0.96

5. 0.04)8.64

6. 8.4)27.72

7. 1.052 × 0.09

8. 0.1924 ÷ 1.3

9. 0.582 ÷ 0.6

10. Shade the decimal square to show the product of 0.7 × 0.3. Label each section.

- Shade and label 0.7 in one color.

- Shade and label 0.3 in another color.

- Use your pencil to shade the area when the sections overlap.

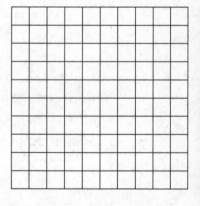

11. Mr. Sims has a new car. The manufacturer says the car should get 32 to 34 miles per gallon in the city. Mr. Sims drove 309.7 miles on 9.5 gallons of gas. How many miles does his car get for each gallon of gas? Is the manufacturer's figure correct? Show your work.

Make It Work

Answer the questions below.

1. $1.63 \times 5.4 =$

A. 1.467 **B.** 8.802

C. 8.82 **D.** 14.67

2. $7.3 \overline{)18.25}$

A. 0.025 **B.** 0.25

C. 2.5 **D.** 25

3. Write a multiplication sentence that represents the model on the right.

_____ _____ _____

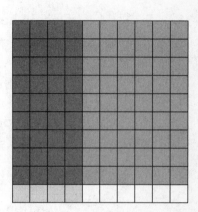

4. Place the decimal point in the quotient of the division on the right. Explain your thinking.

$$
\begin{array}{r}
73 \\
6\overline{)4.38} \\
-4\,2 \\
\hline
18 \\
-18 \\
\hline
0
\end{array}
$$

_____

_____

_____

5. Help Irwin find the quotient of $0.02\overline{)64}$.

○ He needs to change 0.02 to a whole number. How does he do this? Show it in the problem.

_____

_____

○ Does he need to do anything to the dividend, 64? Show in it the problem.

_____

_____

○ Find the quotient. What will he do to 64 to complete the division?

_____

Kick It Up!

Chapter 2

Question 1: How does a number's place affect its value?

Suppose you drew four number cards at random and had to make the greatest or least possible number with them. What would you do? Develop a game that shows how to do this. Your game should include cards for the digits 0-9 and cards for the values in tenths and hundredths places, such as 0.1, 0.01, 0.2, 0.02, and so on.

Decide how the game will begin. Will one player start and draw cards, or will a dealer give cards to all the players? Include different levels for your game, such has whole numbers only, numbers to tenths place, and numbers to hundredths place, or numbers rounded to a certain decimal place.

Think about how players will score or lose points. And, yes, don't forget a written set of rules.

Question 2: What is a power of 10?

Powers of ten can be, well, very powerful. Work on your own or with a partner to explain what a power of 10 is. Then show how powers of 10 can increase the size of a number very quickly.

$$3 \times 10 = 30 \quad 3 \times 10^2 = 300 \quad 3 \times 10^3 = 3,000 \quad 3 \times 10^4 = 30,000$$

Once you decide on an explanation, decide how you will present your information. It could be on a poster, in a short video, or as a graphic comic—whatever you would like. But it needs to include these concepts.

- How do you recognize a power of 10?

- What are exponents?

- How are expressions such as 10^2 and 10^3 different from 10×2 and 10×3?

Question 3: Do you have a "trick" that helps you multiply or divide whole numbers?

Most people have their favorite "tricks" they use when multiplying or dividing whole numbers. Sometimes another person's trick doesn't help. At other times it's just what you need. Maybe you don't have a trick but you do have a tip.

Work with a partner and take a survey of your classmates. Ask whether they have a trick they use when multiplying or dividing whole numbers. If they don't, ask whether they have a tip for their fellow mathematicians. Record all suggestions. Add your own. Then make two numbered lists, one for each operation. Explain each trick and show an example if necessary.

Multiplication and Division Tricks and Tips	
Multiplication	Division
1. Always use placeholder zeros.	1. Estimate the answer first.

Place a copy of the lists in the math area of your classroom. If possible, provide each of your classmates with a copy.

Question 4: Can you model operations with decimal numbers?

Sometimes a model, or a visual representation, helps more than words. Work with three partners to make a booklet called *Modeling Operations with Decimals*. Do research to find the best model for each operation.

Decide how to divide the work. Will each student work on a different model? Will pairs of students do two models? Will everyone work on all the models? Once you have decided, start to work. For each operation, include:

- a sample model

- an explanation of the sample

- some rules for how to create a model for a given expression

You may want to explain that models are best limited to equations with smaller numbers. If the numbers have more than three digits, the model may be too complex to be helpful.

Lesson 19 — Adding and Subtracting Fractions With Unlike Denominators

5.NF.1   Add and subtract fractions with unlike denominators (including mixed numbers) by replacing given fractions with equivalent fractions in such a way as to produce an equivalent sum or difference of fractions with like denominators. *For example,* $\frac{2}{3} + \frac{5}{4} = \frac{8}{12} + \frac{15}{12} = \frac{23}{12}$. $\left(In\ general, \frac{a}{b} + \frac{c}{d} = \frac{(ad\ +\ bc)}{bd}\right)$.

Real World Connections

Many numbers you come across may not be whole numbers. Instead they'll be parts of a whole, or **fractions**. It is important for you to be able to add and subtract them.

Alison ran $\frac{1}{2}$ mile to warm up for soccer practice on Monday. She ran $\frac{2}{3}$ mile on Wednesday. How far did she run in all?

Key Words

fractions
denominator
equivalent
   fractions

$\frac{1}{2}$ $\frac{2}{3}$

The **denominator** is the number on the bottom of the fraction. To add or subtract fractions with unlike denominators, replace the given fractions with **equivalent fractions** that have the same denominator. Two fractions are equivalent if they have the same value when simplified. Once you replace the fractions with equivalent fractions that have the same denominator, you can add the numerators.

When you write an equivalent fraction, you multiply the numerator and denominator by the same nonzero number. To write an addition equation using equivalent fractions that have the same denominator, use this method:

$$\frac{a}{b} + \frac{c}{d} = \frac{(ad + bc)}{bd}$$

Example:

$$\frac{2}{3} + \frac{3}{4} = \frac{(2 \cdot 4) + (3 \cdot 3)}{(3 \cdot 4)} = \frac{8 + 9}{12} = \frac{17}{12} = 1\frac{5}{12}$$

$$\frac{3}{4} - \frac{1}{5} = \frac{(3 \cdot 5) - (4 \cdot 1)}{(4 \cdot 5)} = \frac{15 - 4}{20} = \frac{11}{20}$$

If you have a subtraction equation, you can use the same method. However, replace the plus sign with a minus sign.

Take It Apart

Use a strategy similar to this one to add fractions with unlike denominators. Add $\frac{1}{2}$ mile to $\frac{2}{3}$ mile.

Step 1 Write the problem as an equation.

$$\frac{1}{2} + \frac{2}{3} = ?$$

Step 2 Replace the fractions with equivalent fractions that have the same denominator.

$$\frac{1}{2} + \frac{2}{3} = \frac{(1 \cdot 3) + (2 \cdot 2)}{(2 \cdot 3)} = \frac{3 + 4}{6}$$

Step 3 Add the numerators.

$$\frac{3 + 4}{6} = \frac{7}{6}$$

Step 4 Simplify the result.

$$\frac{7}{6} = 1\frac{1}{6}$$

Step 5 The sum is $1\frac{1}{6}$ miles.

Use the strategy above to fill in the missing numbers.

1. Add: $\frac{8}{5} + \frac{3}{2}$.

$$\frac{8}{5} + \frac{3}{2} = \frac{(8 \cdot \underline{\hspace{1cm}}) + (\underline{\hspace{1cm}} \cdot 3)}{(5 \cdot \underline{\hspace{1cm}})}$$

$$= \frac{(\underline{\hspace{1cm}} + 15)}{\underline{\hspace{1cm}}} = \frac{31}{\underline{\hspace{1cm}}}$$

2. Subtract: $\frac{5}{4} - \frac{1}{3}$.

$$\frac{5}{4} - \frac{1}{3} = \frac{(\underline{\hspace{1cm}} \cdot 3) - (4 \cdot \underline{\hspace{1cm}})}{(\underline{\hspace{1cm}} \cdot 3)}$$

$$= \frac{(\underline{\hspace{1cm}} - 4)}{\underline{\hspace{1cm}}} = \frac{11}{\underline{\hspace{1cm}}}$$

Put It Together

Now use what you know to evaluate these expressions using equivalent fractions with the same denominators. Show your work.

1. $\frac{1}{6} + \frac{5}{7}$

2. $\frac{5}{4} - \frac{1}{2}$

3. $\frac{4}{5} + \frac{3}{8}$

4. $\frac{5}{9} - \frac{1}{8}$

5. $\frac{8}{5} + \frac{4}{3}$

6. $\frac{5}{3} - \frac{9}{7}$

Answer the questions. Talk about your answers with the class.

7. Brody added a fraction to $\frac{5}{6}$ to get $\frac{31}{30}$. Use the equation $\frac{a}{b} + \frac{c}{d} = \frac{(ad + bc)}{bd}$ to find the fraction he added.

8. Mariah subtracted $\frac{2}{7}$ from $\frac{10}{9}$. She found a difference of 4. What mistake did she make, and how can you correct it to find the right answer?

Make It Work

Answer the questions below.

1. Which fraction is equivalent to $\frac{2}{7}$?

    A. $\frac{9}{27}$ **B.** $\frac{4}{9}$

    C. $\frac{7}{2}$ **D.** $\frac{10}{35}$

2. What is the sum of $\frac{2}{9} + \frac{3}{5}$?

    A. $\frac{5}{14}$ **B.** $\frac{37}{45}$

    C. $\frac{5}{45}$ **D.** $\frac{14}{6}$

3. Geraldine served $\frac{19}{8}$ pies at a party. If she started with 5 pies, how much does she have left over?

_____

_____

_____

4. Kylie has $2\frac{1}{2}$ gallons of blue paint. Sarah has $1\frac{1}{4}$ gallons of white paint. They are going to mix the paint to make light blue. How much light blue paint will they have?

_____

_____

_____

_____

5. Carlos used the equation $\frac{a}{b} + \frac{c}{d} = \frac{(ad + bc)}{bd}$ to find the sum of the fractions $\frac{5}{6} + \frac{2}{3}$. Show that he can also find the sum by rewriting only one fraction and adding the numerators. Tell which method you think is easier for solving the problem.

_____

_____

_____

_____

_____

Lesson 20 Solving Word Problems Involving Adding and Subtracting Fractions

5.NF.2 Solve word problems involving addition and subtraction of fractions referring to the same whole, including cases of unlike denominators, e.g., by using visual fraction models or equations to represent the problem. Use benchmark fractions and number sense of fractions to estimate mentally and assess the reasonableness of answers. *For example, recognize an incorrect result* $\frac{2}{5} + \frac{1}{2} = \frac{3}{7}$, *by observing that* $\frac{3}{7} < \frac{1}{2}$.

Real World Connections

Key Words

equation

variable

You often need to work with parts of a whole. Suppose, for example, you are planting different kinds of flowers in parts of a garden. It will help to understand how to divide the garden into parts so you can buy and plant the right flowers.

Megan's class is planting a garden. They are planting $\frac{1}{3}$ of the garden with sunflowers and $\frac{1}{6}$ of the garden with roses. The rest of the garden will be filled with daisies. What fraction of the garden will be filled with daisies?

One way to add and subtract fractions from word problems is to write an **equation**. Recall that an equation is a mathematical sentence that shows that two numbers or expressions are equal. A **variable**, shown as a letter, represents the number you want to find in an equation.

Another way to add and subtract fractions is to use a visual model. A model should be divided into sections according to the denominator of a fraction. The number of sections indicated by the numerator should be shaded. A model is a drawing that helps you picture the addition or subtraction problem.

For example, Katarina spent $\frac{1}{3}$ of her birthday money on a book and $\frac{2}{9}$ of her birthday money on a toy. How much of her birthday money did she spend?

Write the problem as an equation.

Let x = the amount she spent

$\frac{1}{3} + \frac{2}{9} = x$

$\frac{(1 \cdot 9) + (3 \cdot 2)}{(3 \cdot 9)} = \frac{9 + 6}{27} = \frac{15}{27} = \frac{5}{9}$

Take It Apart

Use a strategy similar to this one to add and subtract fractions in word problems. Add $\frac{1}{3}$ sunflowers to $\frac{1}{6}$ roses. Then subtract the total from 1 whole to find the fraction of daisies, *d*.

Step 1 Identify the fractions in the word problem.

Decide which operation(s) to use.

Fractions: $\frac{1}{3}$ and $\frac{1}{6}$ Operations: addition, then subtraction

Step 2 Write the problem as an equation.

$$d = 1 - \left(\frac{1}{3} + \frac{1}{6}\right)$$

Step 3 Add the fractions first.

$$\frac{1}{3} + \frac{1}{6} = \frac{(1 \cdot 6) + (3 \cdot 1)}{(3 \cdot 6)} = \frac{(6 + 3)}{18} = \frac{9}{18} = \frac{1}{2}$$

Step 4 Subtract from 1.

$$= \frac{2}{2} - \frac{1}{2} = \frac{1}{2}$$ They will plant daisies in $\frac{1}{2}$ the garden.

Step 5 Decide if your answer is reasonable.

$\frac{1}{3} < \frac{1}{2}$ $\frac{1}{6} < \frac{1}{2}$ The answer is reasonable.

Use the strategy above to write equations to solve each word problem. Then estimate which whole numbers the answer should fall between.

1. Gina used $1\frac{1}{4}$ cups of flour to bake cookies and $2\frac{1}{3}$ cups to bake a cake. How many cups of flour, *f*, did she use in all?

   _____

   _____

2. Sage has $5\frac{6}{7}$ pounds of potting soil. He used $2\frac{1}{3}$ pounds for his plants. How many pounds of potting soil, *s*, does he have left?

   _____

   _____

3. Marlene bought $2\frac{5}{6}$ pounds of grapes. She gave $1\frac{1}{5}$ pounds away to her friends. How many pounds of grapes, g, does she have left?

   _____

   _____

4. Hector practiced $\frac{3}{4}$ hour for the talent show on Friday and $1\frac{2}{5}$ hours on Saturday. How many hours, *p*, did he practice in all?

   _____

   _____

 **Put It Together**

Write and solve an equation that describes each model.

1.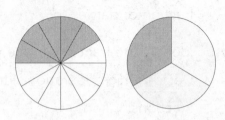

_____

2.

_____

Add or subtract fractions to solve each problem.

3. Josiah ate three-eighths of his orange before his soccer game. He ate one third of the orange during half-time. How much of the orange did he eat in all?

_____

4. Theresa made five-sixths of a pound of chocolate. One-third pound of the chocolate had nuts in it. How much of the chocolate did not have nuts?

_____

5. Rafael put seven-tenths of a cup of raisins and one-quarter cup of pretzels in a bowl to make a trail mix. How many cups did he have in all?

_____

6. Christina ate one-eighth of a pizza for dinner. Abigail ate one-quarter of the pizza. If the pizza had 8 slices, how many slices are left?

_____

Make It Work

Answer the questions below.

1. Chloe spent $\frac{4}{9}$ of her allowance. What fraction of her allowance does she have left?

   A. $\frac{2}{5}$ C. $\frac{8}{9}$

   B. $\frac{5}{9}$ D. $\frac{9}{5}$

2. The school track is $\frac{4}{5}$ of a mile long. If Raheem jogged around it twice, how far did he run?

   A. $\frac{4}{7}$ C. $\frac{6}{5}$

   B. $\frac{8}{10}$ D. $\frac{8}{5}$

3. Darby is making a smoothie according to the recipe. How many cups will the recipe make?

Fresh Fruit Smoothie

$\frac{3}{4}$ c Strawberries

$\frac{1}{2}$ c Blueberries

$\frac{1}{8}$ c Orange juice

$\frac{1}{4}$ c Crushed ice

$\frac{1}{4}$ c Sparkling water

_____

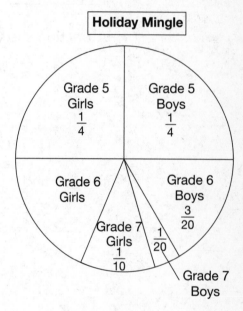

4. The circle graph shows the fractions of students who went to the Holiday Mingle. What fraction consisted of Grade 6 girls?

_____

5. Myling collects stamps. Explain how to find the perimeter, or distance around, this stamp.

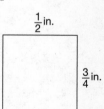

_____

_____

_____

_____

Lesson 21 Interpreting Fractions as Division

5.NF.3 Interpret a fraction as division of the numerator by the denominator $\left(\frac{a}{b} = a \div b\right)$. Solve word problems involving division of whole numbers leading to answers in the form of fractions or mixed numbers, e.g., by using visual fraction models or equations to represent the problem. For example, interpret $\frac{3}{4}$ as the result of dividing 3 by 4, noting that $\frac{3}{4}$ multiplied by 4 equals 3, and that when 3 wholes are shared equally among 4 people each person has a share of size $\frac{3}{4}$. If 9 people want to share a 50-pound sack of rice equally by weight, how many pounds of rice should each person get? Between what two whole numbers does your answer lie?

Real World Connections

Fractions and mixed numbers are useful for solving problems involving division.

> A gardener has to divide 30 pounds of soil equally among 7 plants. How many pounds of soil can the gardener give to each plant? Between which two numbers does your answer lie?

A **fraction** shows division of the numerator by the denominator.

$$\frac{a}{b} = a \div b$$

$$\frac{1}{2} = 1 \div 2 = 0.5 \qquad \frac{3}{4} = 3 \div 4 = 0.75 \qquad \frac{2}{5} = 2 \div 5 = 0.4$$

Division and multiplication are related as shown.

$$\frac{1}{2} \times 2 = 1 \qquad \frac{3}{4} \times 4 = 3 \qquad \frac{2}{5} \times 5 = 2$$

Take It Apart

To figure out how much soil to give to each plant, follow these steps.

Step 1 Identify the numbers being divided.

30 lb divided by 7 plants

30 ÷ 7

Step 2 Write the division problem as a fraction.

$\frac{30}{7}$

Step 3 Convert the improper fraction to a mixed number.

$4\frac{2}{7}$ lb

Step 4 Find the next lowest and next highest whole number.

$4 < 4\frac{2}{7} < 5$

Each plant should get between 4 and 5 pounds of soil.

Use the strategy above to write each fraction as a division expression.

1. $\frac{9}{10}$ _____

2. $\frac{2}{7}$ _____

3. $\frac{1}{8}$ _____

4. $\frac{12}{5}$ _____

5. $\frac{26}{8}$ _____

6. $\frac{8}{14}$ _____

 Put It Together

Use what you know about fractions to answer each question.

1. What number will you get when you multiply $\frac{2}{3}$ by 3 wholes? _____

2. What number will you get when you multiply $\frac{5}{9}$ by 9 wholes? _____

3. What number can you multiply by $\frac{6}{7}$ to get 6? _____

4. What number can you multiply by $\frac{11}{13}$ to get 11? _____

Draw a line to connect each fraction to the problem it solves.

5. Scott has 3 hours to study 6 subjects.
   If he divides his time evenly, how long $\frac{1}{3}$
   can he study for each subject?

6. Jasmine wants to divide 7 pounds of
   chocolate evenly among 21 students. $\frac{1}{2}$
   How much will each student get?

Answer the questions. Share your ideas with a classmate.

7. Mr. Franks gave pies to his friends. If seven pies were shared equally among 9 friends, how much did each person get?

   _____

8. Ms. Taylor needs to divide 12 kilograms of an unknown sample evenly among 15 students. How much of the sample will each student get?

   _____

Make It Work

Answer the questions below.

1. A 25-lb bag of flour is divided evenly between 7 chefs. Between which two numbers is the amount of flour each chef gets?

   A. 1 and 2 lb

   B. 2 and 3 lb

   C. 3 and 4 lb

   D. 5 and 6 lb

2. The zookeeper has a 60-lb bag of food to divide evenly among 9 giraffes. Between which two numbers is the amount each giraffe gets?

   A. 3 and 4 lb

   B. 4 and 5 lb

   C. 5 and 6 lb

   D. 6 and 7 lb

3. Trina is dividing 12 pounds of fruit into 5 identical bowls of fruit salad. About how many pounds of fruit does she put into each bowl?

   _____

4. The Lopez family cell phone plan has 200 minutes. If the minutes are divided evenly among three children, how many minutes does each child get?

   _____

5. Mr. Lee's car travels 25 miles per gallon of gas. Write a fraction to find how many gallons he needs to travel 375 miles. Explain.

   _____

   _____

   _____

5.NF.3 Interpret a fraction as division of the numerator by the denominator $\left(\frac{a}{b} = a \div b\right)$. Solve word problems involving division of whole numbers leading to answers in the form of fractions or mixed numbers, e.g., by using visual fraction models or equations to represent the problem. *For example, interpret $\frac{3}{4}$ as the result of dividing 3 by 4, noting that $\frac{3}{4}$ multiplied by 4 equals 3, and that when 3 wholes are shared equally among 4 people each person has a share of size $\frac{3}{4}$. If 9 people want to share a 50-pound sack of rice equally by weight, how many pounds of rice should each person get? Between what two whole numbers does your answer lie?*

Real World Connections

In the previous lesson, you learned that fractions can be interpreted as division and can be used to solve problems involving division. Now you will expand on what you've learned to solve different kinds of problems that lead to answers in the form of fractions and mixed numbers.

> Mrs. Rodriguez brought 5 liters of sports drink to the game. If 14 players want to share it evenly among themselves, how much will each player get?

It is important to be able to change fractions to different forms to solve some types of problems. A **mixed number** is written as a whole number and a fraction. An **improper fraction** has a numerator greater than the denominator. Make sure you know how to convert between mixed numbers and improper fractions.

To change a mixed number to an improper fraction, you can multiply and add.

$$2\frac{1}{4} \longrightarrow \frac{(2 \times 4) + 1}{4} = \frac{9}{4}$$

To change an improper fraction to a mixed number, you can divide and subtract.

$$\frac{18}{7} \longrightarrow 18 \div 7 = \text{between 2 and 3}$$

$$2 \times 7 = 14 \qquad 18 - 14 = 4$$

$$2\frac{4}{7}$$

Toolbox

pencil

Key Words

mixed number

improper fraction

Take It Apart

To figure out how much each player will get, follow some simple steps.

Step 1 Identify the numbers being divided.

5 L divided by 14 players

5 ÷ 14

Step 2 Write the division problem as a fraction.

$\frac{5}{14}$

Each player will get $\frac{5}{14}$ L of sports drink.

Use the strategy above to express each quotient as a fraction.

1. 5 ÷ 8 _____

2. 10 ÷ 12 _____

3. 2 ÷ 3 _____

4. 14 ÷ 19 _____

5. $\frac{8}{9} \div \frac{4}{9}$ _____

6. $\frac{4}{5} \div \frac{3}{5}$ _____

 Put It Together

Express each phrase as a fraction.

1. 6 meters of fabric divided evenly among 10 dancers _____

2. 15 pounds of clay divided evenly among 22 art students _____

3. 8 cups of sugar divided evenly among 5 cakes _____

4. 50 gallons of gasoline divided evenly among 3 race cars _____

5. 4 pounds of taffy divided evenly among 9 friends _____

6. 182 kilometers divided evenly among 4 hours _____

Answer the questions. Share your ideas with a classmate.

7. A bottle contains 10 ounces of medicine. How many doses are in the bottle if each dose is $1\frac{1}{2}$ ounces?

   _____

8. A box contains 28 ounces of cereal. How many servings are in the box if each serving is $3\frac{1}{2}$ ounces?

   _____

     Peoples Common Core Mathematics

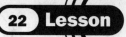

Make It Work

Answer the questions below.

1. A toy company has 12 pounds of stuffing to divide evenly among 25 soft animals. Find how much stuffing each animal will get. Between which two numbers does the answer lie?

   A. 3 and 4 lb

   B. 2 and 3 lb

   C. 1 and 2 lb

   D. 0 and 1 lb

2. A landscaper has 38 pounds of mulch to divide evenly among 12 flower beds. Find how much mulch will go in each flower bed. Between which two numbers does the answer lie?

   A. 3 and 4 lb

   B. 4 and 5 lb

   C. 5 and 6 lb

   D. 6 and 7 lb

3. Kyle mows 3 lawns in an hour. How long will it take him to mow 19 lawns?

   _____

4. A builder has 120 cubic yards of cement. It will be divided evenly among 7 lamp posts. How much cement will go into each lamp post?

   _____

5. Nine friends want to share 2 gallons of ice cream. Explain how they can decide how much each friend should get if they want to share evenly.

   _____

   _____

5.NF.4.a Interpret the product $\left(\frac{a}{b}\right) \times q$ as a parts of a partition of q into b equal parts; equivalently, as the result of a sequence of operations $a \times q \div b$. For example, use a visual fraction model to show $\left(\frac{2}{3}\right) \times 4 = \frac{8}{3}$, and create a story context for this equation. Do the same with $\left(\frac{2}{3}\right) \times \left(\frac{4}{5}\right) = \frac{8}{15}$. $\left(\text{In general, } \left(\frac{a}{b}\right) \times \left(\frac{c}{d}\right) = \frac{ac}{bd}\right)$.

Real World Connections

Toolbox

pencil

Key Word

product

To solve many real-life problems, you need to multiply a fraction by a whole number or by another fraction. Understanding how the products are formed will help you solve these types of problems.

> Kayla goes to gymnastics practice for 3 hours. She spends $\frac{2}{5}$ of the practice working on her floor routine. How long does she spend working on the floor routine?

Remember that a **product** is the answer you get when you multiply numbers together. The numbers you multiply can be whole numbers or fractions.

To find the product of fractions, multiply the numerators. Then multiply the denominators.

$$\frac{a}{b} \times \frac{c}{d} = \frac{ac}{bd}$$

$$\frac{1}{4} \times \frac{2}{5} = \frac{2}{20} = \frac{1}{10}$$

You can rewrite a whole number as a fraction with a denominator of 1.

$$\frac{a}{b} \times q = \frac{a}{b} \times \frac{q}{1} = \frac{aq}{b}$$

$$\frac{2}{3} \times 7 = \frac{14}{3} = 4\frac{2}{3}$$

Take It Apart

To figure out how long Kayla spends working on her floor routine, follow these steps.

Step 1 List the information you know.

Gymnastics practice is 3 hours.

$\frac{2}{5}$ of practice is on floor routine.

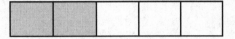

Step 2 Write an equation.

$\frac{2}{5} \times 3 =$ time on floor routine

Step 3 Solve.

$\frac{2}{5} \times 3 = \frac{2}{5} \times \frac{3}{1} = \frac{(2 \times 3)}{5} = \frac{6}{5}$

Step 4 Simplify the answer.

$\frac{6}{5}$ is an improper fraction. Convert to a mixed number.

$\frac{6}{5} = 1\frac{1}{5}$

She spends $1\frac{1}{5}$ hours working on her floor routine.

Use the strategy above to find each product.

1. $\frac{x}{y} \times z =$ _____

2. $a \times \frac{d}{e} =$ _____

3. $\frac{f}{g} \times h =$ _____

4. $\frac{p}{q} \times r =$ _____

5. $l \times \frac{m}{n} =$ _____

6. $\frac{s}{t} \times u =$ _____

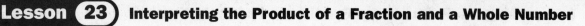

Lesson 23 **Interpreting the Product of a Fraction and a Whole Number**

 Put It Together

Use what you know about multiplication of fractions to find each product. Simplify your answer to lowest terms or to a mixed number.

1. $\frac{3}{4} \times 8 =$ _____

2. $\frac{9}{10} \times \frac{1}{2} =$ _____

3. $\frac{1}{2} \times \frac{5}{6} =$ _____

4. $\frac{1}{4} \times \frac{2}{5} =$ _____

5. $3 \times \frac{3}{8} =$ _____

6. $\frac{6}{7} \times 14 =$ _____

Answer the questions. Share your ideas with a classmate.

7. Tony read $\frac{3}{4}$ of the book he is completing for a report. He read $\frac{1}{3}$ of that on the school bus. How much of the book did Tony read on the school bus?

_____

8. Keisha is making pom-poms for the cheerleading squad. She needs 18 strips of ribbon for one pom-pom. Each strip is $\frac{13}{2}$ inches long. What is the total length of ribbon she needs for each pom-pom, in feet?

_____

9. Tonya ran $\frac{9}{10}$ of a mile. Her sister ran half as far. How many miles did Tonya's sister run?

_____

Make It Work

Answer the questions below.

1. Angelina is making a photo album. She can fit 8 photos on each page. If a page is $\frac{3}{4}$ full, how many more photos can she fit?

   A. 1   **B.** 3

   C. 2   **D.** 4

2. If $5x = 4$, what is the value of x?

   A. $\frac{1}{4}$ **B.** $\frac{5}{4}$

   C. $\frac{1}{5}$ **D.** $\frac{4}{5}$

3. Lanie has 32 students in her drama class. If $\frac{3}{8}$ of the students are boys, how many boys are in drama class?

_____

4. Eduardo has this recipe, but he wants to use only $\frac{2}{3}$ of the sugar listed. How many cups of sugar should he use?

   Brownies

   1 stick butter
   2 c sugar
   3 eggs
   10 tbsp cocoa powder
   2 c flour
   1 tsp vanilla

_____

5. Is the product of two proper fractions always less than or greater than one? Explain and give an example.

_____

_____

_____

_____

Lesson 24 Finding Areas of Rectangles With Fractional Side Lengths

5.NF.4.b Find the area of a rectangle with fractional side lengths by tiling it with unit squares of the appropriate unit fraction side lengths, and show that the area is the same as would be found by multiplying the side lengths. Multiply fractional side lengths to find areas of rectangles, and represent fraction products as rectangular areas.

Real World Connections

Toolbox

pencil
calculator

Key Word

area

Measurements in real life are not always whole numbers. It is important to know how to work with fractional measurements. For example, suppose you need to describe a rectangle for which the length and width are described by fractions. You can use what you know about multiplying fractions.

The **area** of a rectangle is equal to its length multiplied by its width. So if the length of a rectangle is 10 units and the width is 5 units, the area is 50 square units. You can apply the same idea to find the area of a rectangle if the length and width are fractional measurements.

This rectangle is a square that measures 1 unit by 1 unit.

Its area is 1 unit × 1 unit = 1 unit²

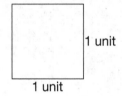

You can divide the figure into 3 sections in one direction and 2 sections in the other direction.

The area of the shaded part of the rectangle is $\frac{2}{3} \times \frac{1}{2} = \frac{2}{6} = \frac{1}{3}$.

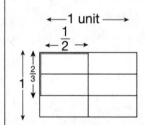

$\frac{2}{6} = \frac{1}{3}$ of the area is colored.

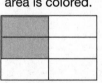

Kara's room is getting new carpet and she needs to know the area of her room to buy new carpet. The carpet she wants costs $8 per square meter. If her room is $4\frac{1}{2}$ m long and $3\frac{1}{3}$ m wide, how much will the carpet cost?

Take It Apart

To figure out how much Kara will pay for new carpet, follow these steps.

Step 1 List the dimensions of her room.

$$l = 4\frac{1}{2} \text{ m}$$

$$w = 3\frac{1}{3} \text{ m}$$

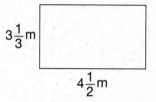

$3\frac{1}{3}$m

$4\frac{1}{2}$m

Step 2 Convert each measurement to an improper fraction.

$$l = 4\frac{1}{2} \text{ m} = \frac{9}{2}$$

$$w = 3\frac{1}{3} \text{ m} = \frac{10}{3}$$

Step 3 Find the area.

$$A = l \times w = \frac{9}{2} \times \frac{10}{3} = \frac{90}{6} = \frac{30}{2} = 15 \text{ m}^2$$

Step 4 Multiply the area by the price of the carpet.

$$\frac{15 \text{ m}^2 \times \$8}{\text{m}^2} = \$120$$

Kara will need to spend $120 for new carpet in her room.

Use the strategy above to find the area of each rectangle.

1.

$6\frac{1}{2}$m

$8\frac{1}{3}$m

_____

2.

$\frac{3}{4}$cm

$\frac{1}{2}$cm

_____

Put It Together

Use what you know about area to fill in the missing values in the tables.

	length	width	area
1.	$\frac{5}{6}$	_____	$\frac{5}{12}$
2.	_____	$\frac{3}{4}$	$\frac{1}{2}$
3.	$\frac{12}{5}$	$\frac{10}{9}$	_____
4.	$\frac{7}{2}$	_____	$\frac{35}{3}$
5.	$8\frac{1}{4}$	$3\frac{1}{3}$	_____
6.	_____	$1\frac{11}{12}$	$\frac{46}{5}$

Answer the questions. Share your ideas with a classmate.

7. A factory adds rectangular metal fasteners to car doors. Each fastener is $\frac{3}{4}$ inch long and $\frac{2}{3}$ inch wide. What is the area of each fastener?

_____

8. The top of Sam's desk is $2\frac{5}{8}$ feet long and $1\frac{2}{3}$ feet wide. If Sam needs to clean the top of his desk, what area is he cleaning?

_____

9. Jenna has two poster boards to choose from for her science project. She needs as much space as possible to present her information. Which poster board has the greater area? Explain.

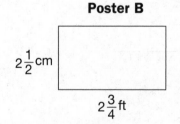

Poster A $3\frac{1}{3}$ cm $1\frac{1}{2}$ ft

Poster B $2\frac{1}{2}$ cm $2\frac{3}{4}$ ft

_____

Make It Work

Answer the questions below.

1. The length of a rectangle is $\frac{6}{8}$ kilometers and the width is $1\frac{2}{3}$ kilometers. What is the area of the rectangle?

A. $\frac{4}{5}$ km²   **B.** 1 km²

C. $1\frac{1}{4}$ km²   **D.** $2\frac{5}{12}$ km²

2. The area of a rectangle is 24 ft². Which measurements might describe its length and width?

A. $4\frac{1}{5}$ ft × $5\frac{5}{7}$ ft   **B.** $2\frac{1}{3}$ ft × $3\frac{3}{4}$ ft

C. $6\frac{2}{5}$ ft × $3\frac{1}{8}$ ft   **D.** $12\frac{1}{2}$ ft × $1\frac{2}{9}$ ft

3. John needs to cover a window with a layer of plastic. The plastic costs $0.50 per square inch. If the window is $10\frac{2}{3}$ inches long and $10\frac{1}{2}$ inches wide, how much will it cost to cover the window in plastic?

_____

4. The width of a rectangle is $1\frac{1}{8}$ m. The area is $\frac{81}{32}$ m². What is the perimeter of, or distance around, the rectangle?

_____

5. Chase needs to find the area of a rectangle that is $2\frac{1}{2}$ yards long and $1\frac{1}{2}$ yards wide. Show that tiling the rectangle with $\frac{1}{2}$-yard unit squares results in the same area as multiplying length times width.

_____

_____

_____

Lesson 25 Comparing Products to Factors

5.NF.5.a   Comparing the size of a product to the size of one factor on the basis of the size of the other factor, without performing the indicated multiplication.

Real World Connections

Toolbox

pencil

Key Words

product

factors

When you multiply numbers together, the answer you get depends on the relationship between the numbers. The answer will change if one of the numbers changes. Knowing how these relationships work can help you make predictions about the answers without even performing the multiplication.

> Theresa invited 9 friends to her birthday party. She wants to buy party favors for each friend. She thought the price of each favor was $2.50, but it turned out that the actual price is $5. How will the change in price affect the total cost of the party favors?

The answer you get when you multiply numbers together is called the **product**. The numbers you multiply to get the product are called **factors**. Changing the size of one factor will change the size of the product. Sometimes you can use the change in one of the factors to predict the answer. Look at the examples below.

$1 \times 8 = 8$ The original product is 8.

$10 \times 8 = 80$ One factor is multiplied by 10. The product is also multiplied by 10.

$100 \times 8 = 800$ One factor is multiplied by 100. The product is also multiplied by 100.

Take It Apart

To figure out how the change in price affects the cost of the party favors, follow some simple steps.

Step 1 Find the initial price of the party favors.

$9 \times \$2.50 = \$22.50$

Step 2 Identify the change in the factor.

$\$2.50$ $\$5.00$ The factor doubles.

Step 3 Predict the change to the product.

If one factor doubles, the product will double as well.

Step 4 Check your prediction.

$9 \times \$5 = \$45$ $45 \div 22.50 = 2$

Theresa will need to spend twice as much as she planned on the party favors.

Use the strategy above to write the missing number that can be used to find the product.

1. $6 \times 12 = 72$

   $3 \times 12 = \underline{\hspace{1cm}} \times 72$

2. $\frac{1}{2} \times 26 = 13$

   $2 \times 26 = \underline{\hspace{1cm}} \times 13$

3. $5 \times 18 = 90$

   $5 \times 6 = \underline{\hspace{1cm}} \times 90$

4. $10 \times 2.5 = 25$

   $100 \times 2.5 = \underline{\hspace{1cm}} \times 25$

5. $\frac{2}{3} \times \frac{1}{2} = \frac{1}{3}$

   $\frac{4}{9} \times \frac{1}{2} = \underline{\hspace{1cm}} \times \frac{1}{3}$

6. $4.6 \times 1.2 = 5.52$

   $4.6 \times 3.6 = \underline{\hspace{1cm}} \times 5.52$

Put It Together

Use what you know about factors and products to answer each question.

1. Two brothers won bags of fish at a carnival. There were 2 fish in each bag. How would the total number of fish change if there were 4 fish in each bag? _____

2. Three buses for a class trip each took 18 students. How will the total number of students change if each bus carries 27 students? _____

3. Four children are playing tennis together. They each brought 3 tennis balls. How many balls must each child bring if the total number of tennis balls is tripled? _____

4. Mr. DiPaolo bought 2 dozen eggs. How does the total number of good eggs change if he discovers that there are 6 broken eggs in each package? _____

5. Emily is putting shoes on the 3 horses at the stable. How will the number of horseshoes change if the number of horses increases to 12? _____

6. Ms. Hastings is on a special diet. Instead of eating 3 meals each day, she must eat 6 smaller meals. How is her total number of meals each week affected? _____

Answer the questions. Share your ideas with a classmate.

7. Louis collects rocks and stores them in small boxes. He has 120 rocks and keeps 6 rocks in each box. How will the number of boxes change if he decides to keep twice as many rocks in each box? Show multiplication equations to support your answer.

_____

_____

_____

8. Antonio is placing an ad in the local phone book. Ads cost $25 per square inch. His old ad was 4 inches by 6 inches. He needs to decrease the cost to $300. What are the possible dimensions of his new ad?

_____

_____

_____

Make It Work

Answer the questions below.

1. If 14 × 6 = 84, which factors will have a product that is half as great?

   A. 7 × 3

   B. 14 × 3

   C. 14 × 2

   D. 7 × 12

2. If 3.5 × 8 = 28, which factors will have a product that is twice as great?

   A. 7 × 16

   B. 3.5 × 4

   C. 7 × 8

   D. 3.5 × 2

3. The area of the rectangle is the product of its length and width. How will the area be affected if the length is multiplied by $1\frac{1}{2}$?

10 m

20 m

_____

_____

4. Use arrays to show that the product doubles if one of the factors doubles.

_____

_____

_____

_____

5. The product of x and x is x^2. Explain how doubling x affects the product. How does tripling x affect the product? Support your answer with an example.

_____

_____

_____

5.NF.5.b Explaining why multiplying a given number by a fraction greater than 1 results in a product greater than the given number (recognizing multiplication by whole numbers greater than 1 as a familiar case); explaining why multiplying a given number by a fraction less than 1 results in a product smaller than the given number; and relating the principle of fraction equivalence $\frac{a}{b} = \frac{(n \times a)}{(n \times b)}$ to the effect of multiplying $\frac{a}{b}$ by 1.

Real World Connections

Toolbox

pencil

Without knowing the actual product of a fraction and another number, you can tell a lot about the product. Knowing the relationships between fractional factors and products can help you understand the product even before performing the calculation.

On Saturday, 215 cars parked in the community lot. Of those cars, $\frac{2}{5}$ were parked by parents bringing their children to soccer practice. Was the number of cars there because of soccer practice greater or less than 215? How do you know?

Multiplying a given number by a fraction that is greater than 1 always results in a product that is greater than the given number. For example,	Multiplying a given number by a fraction that is less than 1 always results in a product that is less than the given number. For example,
$\frac{5}{2} \times 3 = \frac{15}{2} = 7\frac{1}{2}$ $\qquad 7\frac{1}{2} > 3$	$\frac{2}{3} \times 9 = \frac{18}{3} = 6$ $\qquad 6 < 9$
$\frac{8}{3} \times 6 = \frac{48}{3} = 16$ $\qquad 16 > 6$	$\frac{5}{7} \times 6 = \frac{30}{7} = 4\frac{2}{7}$ $\qquad 4\frac{2}{7} < 6$

Take It Apart

To make a prediction about the number of cars, follow some simple steps.

Step 1   Identify the factors being multiplied.

$\frac{2}{5} \times 215$

Step 2   Compare the fraction to 1.

$\frac{2}{5} < 1$

Step 3   Predict what you can about the product.

The factor is less than 1, so the product will be less than 215.

Step 4   Check your prediction.

$\frac{2}{5} \times 215 = \frac{430}{5} = 86$ $86 < 215$

Of the 215 cars, 86 were there to bring children to soccer practice.

Use the strategy above to write "Greater" if the product will be greater than 1 and "Less" if the product will be less than 1.

1. $\frac{3}{4} \times 1$ _____

2. $\frac{9}{7} \times 1$ _____

3. $\frac{11}{12} \times 1$ _____

4. $\frac{24}{27} \times 1$ _____

5. $\frac{412}{450} \times 1$ _____

6. $\frac{560}{289} \times 1$ _____

7. $\frac{15}{14} \times 1$ _____

8. $\frac{39}{50} \times 1$ _____

Put It Together

Use what you know about fractions to write each expression in the correct category.

1. $\frac{6}{7} \times 10$

2. $\frac{12}{15} \times 36$

3. $\frac{9}{14} \times 24$

4. $\frac{10}{3} \times 3$

5. $\frac{5}{4} \times 8$

6. $\frac{99}{100} \times 100$

Product greater than either whole-number factor	Product less than either whole-number factor

Answer the questions. Share your ideas with a classmate.

7. Jamal used a photocopy machine to change the size of a photo. The dimensions of the photo were multiplied by a factor of $\frac{5}{2}$. Did he shrink or enlarge the photo? Explain how you know.

_____

8. Christine ran around the track at school. She ran 9/10 the distance around the track. Did she run around the track once, more than once, or less than once? Explain how you know.

_____

Make It Work

Answer the questions below.

1. Paul earned a raise at work, so his salary increased. Which factor might his salary have been multiplied by to get his new salary?

   A. $\frac{1}{2}$ **B.** $\frac{4}{3}$

   C. $\frac{3}{4}$ **D.** $\frac{7}{9}$

2. Thea multiplied $\frac{5}{7}$ by another factor to get a product of $\frac{5}{21}$ when simplified. Which number might have been the other factor?

   A. $\frac{1}{3}$ **B.** $\frac{7}{5}$

   C. $\frac{15}{21}$ **D.** $\frac{9}{9}$

3. A builder is changing the deck on a house. Each dimension of the deck will be multiplied by $\frac{7}{4}$ to get the dimensions of the new deck. Is the builder increasing or decreasing the size of the deck? Give the dimensions of the new deck.

   3 yd

   5 yd

   _____

4. Stephen is shorter than his sister. Write a fraction that might relate Stephen's height s to his sister's height h.

   _____

5. Show that multiplying $\frac{x}{y}$ by $\frac{n}{n}$ is the same as multiplying $\frac{x}{y}$ by 1. Use an example to support your answer.

   _____

   _____

   _____

   _____

Lesson 27 Solving Problems Involving Multiplication of Fractions and Mixed Numbers

5.NF.6 Solve real world problems involving multiplication of fractions and mixed numbers, e.g., by using visual fraction models or equations to represent the problem.

Real World Connections

Perhaps you are buying $3\frac{1}{2}$ pounds of fruit or you are measuring $2\frac{1}{4}$ ft of wood. Whatever you do, chances are you might need to work with fractions or mixed numbers. It is important that you know how to represent them in problems and solutions.

> Trevor bought a painting for $150. Two years later, he sold the painting for $2\frac{1}{2}$ times what he paid. What profit did he earn on the painting?

You may sometimes find it helpful to represent problems that involve the multiplication of fractions using a **model.** For example, suppose you want to find $\frac{1}{3}$ of $\frac{1}{3}$. By shading $\frac{1}{3}$ of the model in both directions, you find that the product is the overlapping section. In this case, the overlapping section is $\frac{1}{9}$ of the model.

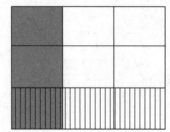

$$\frac{1}{3} \times \frac{1}{3} = \frac{1}{9}$$

Take It Apart

To figure out the profit on the painting, follow these simple steps.

Step 1 List the known information.

He bought the painting for $150.

He sold it for $2\frac{1}{2}$ times $150.

Step 2 Calculate the selling price of the painting.

$2\frac{1}{2} \times \$150 = \frac{5}{2} \times \$150 = \$375$

Step 3 Calculate the difference between the purchase prices and the sale price.

$375 - \$150 = \$225$

Trevor earned a profit of $225 on the painting.

Use the strategy above to calculate the profit or loss given the purchase and sales prices.

1. bought for $85, sold for $1\frac{1}{4}$ times the purchase price _____

2. bought for $200, sold for $2\frac{5}{8}$ times the purchase price _____

3. bought for $350, sold for $\frac{3}{4}$ times the purchase price _____

4. bought for $160, sold for $\frac{4}{5}$ times the purchase price _____

 **Put It Together**

Use what you know about fractions to write an equation to describe each model.

1.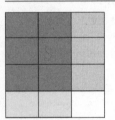

_____

2.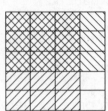

_____

3.

_____

4.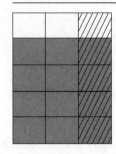

_____

Answer the questions. Share your ideas with a classmate.

5 The coach marked off $\frac{1}{4}$ of the gymnasium for afternoon practices. She marked off $\frac{1}{2}$ of that for the cheerleading squad. In what fraction of the gymnasium can the cheerleading squad practice?

_____

6. In one class, $\frac{3}{7}$ of the students are boys. If there are 28 students, how many girls are in the class?

_____

7. A teacher noted that $\frac{5}{6}$ of her students completed their science projects. If she has 48 students, how many students did not yet complete their science projects?

_____

8. The table shows the weather conditions for the past week. If it rains on the same fraction of days for the next 100 days, about how many days will it rain?

Sun	Mon	Tues	Wed	Thurs	Fri	Sat
Rain	Dry	Rain	Rain	Dry	Dry	Rain

Make It Work

Answer the questions below.

1. Kristin spent $\frac{1}{3}$ of her savings on a new shirt. If her savings were $46.50, how much did she spend on the shirt?

   A. $12.50

   B. $13.00

   C. $15.50

   D. $31.00

2. Benjamin has a recipe that requires 2 cups of flour. He needs to make $3\frac{1}{4}$ times the recipe. How many cups of flour will he need?

   A. $8\frac{1}{2}$ cups

   B. $6\frac{1}{2}$ cups

   C. $5\frac{1}{4}$ cups

   D. $3\frac{1}{4}$ cups

3. Tom and his brother each have to clean $\frac{1}{2}$ of the playroom in their home. Tom's friend offered to clean $\frac{1}{4}$ of Tom's part. What fraction of the room is Tom cleaning?

_____

4. At the local school, $\frac{2}{3}$ of the students in the band are also in the chorus. If there are 44 students in both band and chorus, how many students are in the entire band? Write an equation to solve the problem.

_____

_____

5. A farmer is planting $\frac{1}{3}$ of her field with corn, $\frac{2}{5}$ with wheat, and the rest with lettuce. If the field is 15,000 m², tell the area of the field she planted with each crop. Show how you found the answer.

_____

_____

_____

5.NF.7.a Interpret division of a unit fraction by a non-zero whole number, and compute such quotients. *For example, create a story context for $\left(\frac{1}{3}\right) \div 4$, and use a visual fraction model to show the quotient. Use the relationship between multiplication and division to explain that $\left(\frac{1}{3}\right) \div 4 = \frac{1}{12}$ because $\left(\frac{1}{12}\right) \times 4 = \frac{1}{3}$.*

Real World Connections

Toolbox

pencil

Key Words

unit fraction

reciprocal

You divide objects into smaller parts all the time. Perhaps you divide with friends or divide your time into parts. Sometimes the thing you are dividing is a fraction rather than a whole. You need to know how to divide a fraction by a whole number.

> Mollie had $\frac{1}{3}$ of her birthday cake left over. She and her family decided to share the leftover cake evenly. If there are a total of 4 people in her family, what portion of the original cake will each person get?

A **unit fraction** is a fraction in which the numerator is 1. For example, $\frac{1}{2}$, $\frac{1}{4}$, $\frac{1}{5}$, and $\frac{1}{10}$ are all unit fractions.

You can use models to show the division of a unit fraction by a whole number. This model shows $\frac{1}{2} \div 4$. You can see that each of the 4 parts of the shaded half make up $\frac{1}{8}$ of the entire figure.

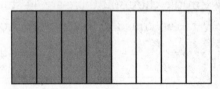

To divide a fraction by a whole number, first convert the whole number to a fraction by giving it a denominator of 1. Then multiply by the reciprocal of the fraction. The **reciprocal** is the fraction inverted.

$$\frac{1}{2} \div 4 = \frac{1}{2} \div \frac{4}{1} = \frac{1}{2} \times \frac{1}{4} = \frac{1}{8}$$

Take It Apart

To figure out how much birthday cake each person gets, follow these steps.

Step 1 Write an expression to represent the problem.

$\frac{1}{3} \div 4$

Step 2 Convert the divisor to a fraction.

$\frac{1}{3} \div \frac{4}{1}$

Step 3 Find the reciprocal of the divisor.

$\frac{4}{1} \longrightarrow \frac{1}{4}$

Step 4 Multiply by the reciprocal of the divisor.

$\frac{1}{3} \times \frac{1}{4} = \frac{1}{12}$

Each person will get $\frac{1}{12}$ of the original cake. It is as if they sliced the original cake into 12 equal pieces.

Use the strategy above to fill in the missing information in each expression.

1. $\frac{1}{5} \div 10 \longrightarrow \frac{1}{5} \times$ _____

2. $\frac{1}{8} \div 14 \longrightarrow$ _____ $\times \frac{1}{14}$

3. $\frac{1}{3} \div$ _____ $\longrightarrow \frac{1}{3} \times \frac{1}{9}$

4. $\frac{1}{2} \div 12 \longrightarrow \frac{1}{2} \times$ _____

5. $\frac{1}{20} \div$ _____ $\longrightarrow \frac{1}{20} \times \frac{1}{5}$

6. $\frac{1}{16} \div 8 \longrightarrow$ _____ $\times \frac{1}{8}$

7. $\frac{1}{4} \div 12 \longrightarrow \frac{1}{4} \times$ _____

8. $\frac{1}{7} \div$ _____ $\longrightarrow \frac{1}{7} \times \frac{1}{6}$

Put It Together

Use what you know about dividing fractions to solve each problem.

1. $\frac{1}{5} \div 3 = $ _____

2. $\frac{1}{9} \div 2 = $ _____

3. $\frac{1}{6} \div 4 = $ _____

4. $\frac{1}{10} \div 5 = $ _____

5. $\frac{1}{3} \div 4 = $ _____

6. $\frac{1}{8} \div 2 = $ _____

Answer the questions. Share your ideas with a classmate.

7. How does the quotient compare to the dividend when you divide a unit fraction by a whole number? Why?

_____

_____

8. A builder has $\frac{1}{2}$ acre of land. He is going to divide it into 3 lots for homes. How large is each lot?

_____

9. Ben's mother brought $\frac{1}{2}$ liter of water to the game. She divided it evenly among her 2 children. How much water did each child get?

_____

10. Marisol has $\frac{1}{3}$ yard of ribbon. She needs to divide it evenly among 6 dresses. How many inches of ribbon can she put on each dress?

_____

Make It Work

Answer the questions below.

1. Mrs. Mahoney wants to divide $\frac{1}{6}$ gallon of milk equally among 5 children. How much milk will each child get?

   A. $\frac{1}{11}$ gal

   B. $\frac{1}{15}$ gal

   C. $\frac{1}{25}$ gal

   D. $\frac{1}{30}$ gal

2. Mr. Hernandez divided $\frac{1}{2}$ pound of chocolate evenly among several children. If each child got $\frac{1}{10}$ lb of chocolate, how many children were there?

   A. 3

   B. 5

   C. 8

   D. 10

3. Cindy has $\frac{1}{3}$ package of fish food. She has to divide it evenly over two weeks. What portion of the package of fish food can she give to the fish each day?

   _____

4. Bryce has $\frac{1}{4}$ pound of sprinkles to put on cakes in a bakery. If he has 8 cakes, how many ounces of sprinkles can he put on each cake? [1 pound = 16 ounces]

   _____

5. What pattern arises when you divide a unit fraction by increasing whole numbers? Give an example to support your answer.

   _____

   _____

Lesson 29 Dividing Whole Numbers by Unit Fractions

5.NF.7.b Interpret division of a whole number by a unit fraction, and compute such quotients. *For example, create a story context for* $4 \div \left(\frac{1}{5}\right)$, *and use a visual fraction model to show the quotient. Use the relationship between multiplication and division to explain that* $4 \div \left(\frac{1}{5}\right) = 20$ *because* $20 \times \left(\frac{1}{5}\right) = 4$.

Real World Connections

Toolbox

pencil

Just as you divided a unit fraction by a whole number, you can divide a whole number by a unit fraction.

Melanie has 16 inches of licorice. If she breaks it up into $\frac{1}{4}$-inch pieces, how many pieces will she have?

Just as you did when you divided unit fractions by whole numbers, you can use models to show the division of a whole number by a unit fraction. This model shows the following division expression.

$$3 \div \frac{1}{4}$$

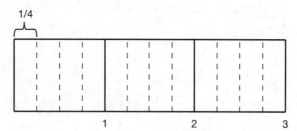

You can see that the 3 wholes are divided into 12 parts that each represents $\frac{1}{4}$.

To divide by a fraction, multiply by the reciprocal of the divisor. Remember that the reciprocal is the fraction inverted.

$$3 \div \frac{1}{4} = 3 \times \frac{4}{1} = 12$$

Take It Apart

To figure out how many pieces of licorice Melanie has, follow these steps.

Step 1 Write an expression to represent the problem.

$16 \div \frac{1}{4}$

Step 2 Convert the dividend to a fraction.

$\frac{16}{1} \div \frac{1}{4}$

Step 3 Find the reciprocal of the divisor.

$\frac{1}{4} \longrightarrow \frac{4}{1}$

Step 4 Multiply by the reciprocal of the divisor.

$\frac{16}{1} \times \frac{4}{1} = 16 \times 4 = 64$

Melanie can divide the licorice into 64 pieces that are each $\frac{1}{4}$-inch long.

Use the strategy above to fill in the missing information in each expression.

1. $5 \div \frac{1}{4} \longrightarrow 5 \times$ _____

2. $8 \div \frac{1}{3} \longrightarrow$ _____ $\times 3$

3. $6 \div$ _____ $\longrightarrow 6 \times 2$

4. $9 \div \frac{1}{15} \longrightarrow$ _____ $\times 5$

5. $12 \div \frac{1}{6} \longrightarrow 12 \times$ _____

6. $20 \div$ _____ $\longrightarrow 20 \times 8$

7. $2 \div \frac{1}{4} \longrightarrow 2 \times$ _____

8. $15 \div$ _____ $\longrightarrow 15 \times 3$

Put It Together

Use what you know about dividing by fractions to solve each problem.

1. $9 \div \frac{1}{3} =$ _____

2. $12 \div \frac{1}{2} =$ _____

3. $6 \div \frac{1}{8} =$ _____

4. $3 \div \frac{1}{3} =$ _____

5. $8 \div \frac{1}{2} =$ _____

6. $14 \div \frac{1}{6} =$ _____

Answer the questions. Share your ideas with a classmate.

7. Justine is cutting a pickle into pieces that are each $\frac{1}{2}$ inch long. If the pickle is 8 inches long, how many pickle pieces will Justine have?

   _____

8. Christian has a wooden board that is 12 feet long. He is cutting it into $\frac{1}{3}$-foot sections. How many sections will he have?

   _____

9. Pedro has a garden that is 8 ft². If each plant requires $\frac{1}{2}$ ft² of space, how many plants can he put in the garden?

   _____

10. A turtle can travel $\frac{1}{4}$ mile per day. How many days will it take the turtle to travel 8 miles?

    _____

Make It Work

Answer the questions below.

1. Leonard has 6 pounds of grapes. He wants to divide them into $\frac{1}{4}$-pound bags. How many bags of grapes can he make?

   A. 4

   B. 10

   C. 16

   D. 24

2. A bag contains 12 cups of trail mix. If each serving is $\frac{1}{5}$ cup, how many servings are in the bag?

   A. 17

   B. 24

   C. 60

   D. 72

3. A bottle contains 12 ounces of medicine. How many $\frac{1}{2}$-ounce doses are in the bottle?

   _____

4. A science teacher began with 3 gallons of pond water. She gave each student $\frac{1}{12}$ gallon for study. If she used up all the water, how many students are in the class?

   _____

5. A factory machine takes $\frac{1}{2}$ second to apply a label on a bottle. How many labels can the machine apply in 10 minutes? Explain how you found your answer.

   _____

   _____

   _____

   _____

   _____

   _____

Lesson 30 Solving Problems Involving Units, Fractions, and Whole Numbers

5.NF.7.c Solve real world problems involving division of unit fractions by non-zero whole numbers and division of whole numbers by unit fractions, e.g., by using visual fraction models and equations to represent the problem. *For example, how much chocolate will each person get if 3 people share $\frac{1}{2}$ lb of chocolate equally? How many $\frac{1}{3}$-cup servings are in 2 cups of raisins?*

Real World Connections

Toolbox

pencil

calculator

In the previous lessons, you practiced dividing unit fractions by whole numbers and whole numbers by unit fractions. Now you will use these skills to solve a variety of real-world problems.

> Maggie bought $\frac{1}{3}$ pound of salmon. She spent $2.00.
> What is the price per pound of salmon?

The key to solving problems involving of and by unit fractions is figuring out the dividend and divisor from the problem. Remember that the dividend is the number being divided. The divisor is the number you are dividing by.

Divide $\frac{1}{3}$ pound of dough into 3 pizzas

$\frac{1}{3} \div 3 = \frac{1}{9}$ lb each

Divide 6 pounds of dough into $\frac{1}{4}$-lb pizzas

$6 \div \frac{1}{4} = 24$ pizzas

Take It Apart

To figure out the price of salmon, follow these steps.

Step 1   Write an equation to represent the problem.

$2 \div \frac{1}{3}$ = the price per pound of salmon

Step 2   Convert the dividend to a fraction.

$\frac{2}{1} \div \frac{1}{3}$ = the price per pound of salmon

Step 3   Find the reciprocal of the divisor.

$\frac{1}{3} \rightarrow \frac{3}{1}$

Step 4   Multiply by the reciprocal of the divisor.

$\frac{2}{1} \times \frac{3}{1} = 2 \times 3 = 6$

The salmon costs $6 per pound.

Use the strategy above to find the missing number.

1. $12 \div \frac{1}{2} =$ _____

2. $\frac{1}{6} \div$ _____ $= \frac{1}{18}$

3. $\frac{1}{4} \div 4 =$ _____

4. $18 \div \frac{1}{6} =$ _____

5. $5 \div$ _____ $= 15$

6. $\frac{1}{3} \div 9 =$ _____

7. $20 \div$ _____ $= 80$

8. $\frac{1}{2} \div 14 =$ _____

 Put It Together

Write an expression that represents each problem.

1. 5 feet of string cut in $\frac{1}{4}$-foot lengths _____

2. 12 degrees Celsius in $\frac{1}{2}$-degree increments _____

3. $\frac{1}{2}$ gallon of juice in 6 cups _____

4. 9 tons of rock in $\frac{1}{3}$ ton loads _____

5. $\frac{1}{4}$ pound of salt in 8 samples _____

6. 10 kilometers in $\frac{1}{6}$ hour _____

Answer the questions. Share your ideas with a classmate.

7. Lynx, a cat, eats $\frac{1}{2}$ cup of food at each meal. If his bag of cat food contains 24 cups of food, how many meals can it serve?

    _____

8. A deli cuts cheddar cheese into $\frac{1}{8}$-pound portions. How many portions can they cut from an 8-pound block of cheese?

    _____

9. Myra has $\frac{1}{4}$ pound of chopped meat. She is going to make it into 6 small hamburgers. What will be the weight of each hamburger?

    _____

Make It Work

Answer the questions below.

1. How many portions can be cut from 5 large sandwiches if each portion is $\frac{1}{6}$ of a sandwich?

   A. 36

   B. 30

   C. 25

   D. 11

2. The art teacher divided $\frac{1}{6}$ pound of clay into balls for the students. If each student received $\frac{1}{48}$ pound of clay, how many students are in the class?

   A. 4

   B. 6

   C. 8

   D. 12

3. A student folds a sheet of paper in half. He then folds the folded paper in half again. Write an equation to show that the student has formed sections of the paper that are each equal to $\frac{1}{4}$ of the total.

_____

4. A landscaper has $\frac{1}{4}$ of a truckload of topsoil. The truck can hold 16 cubic yards of topsoil and each cubic yard weighs 2,400 pounds. How many pounds of topsoil can go into each flower bed if there are 8 flower beds?

_____

5. Explain how you can use division by a unit fraction to figure out how many 8-ounce pieces of turkey are in 5 pounds.

_____

_____

_____

_____

Kick It Up!

Chapter 3

Question 1: How can you model adding and subtracting fractions?

Work with a partner to make a model that you can use to add or subtract fractions. Then write two word problems. One should involve the addition of fractions and one should involve the subtraction of fractions. Be creative in your word problems. Consider including the names of friends, hobbies, or familiar objects. Then use your fraction models to work out the answer to each problem.

Decide on a way to present your work to the class. You might make a video that shows how you use the models to solve the problem. You might write a "How-To" book that outlines the steps for solving the problem.

Once you are ready, present your problems to the class. Explain the process you followed and discuss how you came up with your ideas.

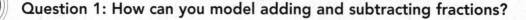

Question 2: How can you share with your friends?

Work with a partner to decide on something you can divide to share with your classmates. It should be something that is a whole material that can be split up into parts, such as an amount of ribbon, chocolate, pizza, or cake. It does not have to be in a form that other students can use or eat.

On a poster board, write out the problem and the solution to divide the material evenly among the students in the class. If time allows, work the problem out in front of the class. Then use whatever tools necessary, such as scissors or a scale, to divide the material according to your solution. With your teacher's permission, distribute the equal portions to the class.

Question 3: How can you enlarge your favorite picture?

For this project, you will enlarge a picture. In the end, you are going to show the class the original picture and the enlarged picture. You are also going to label the fraction by which you increased the dimensions of the picture. You must be able to multiply the original dimensions by a fraction to form the enlargement. To enlarge the picture, you can draw a smaller and a larger picture, you can enlarge a picture on a copy machine, or you can have a photograph enlarged at a store or online.

     Peoples Common Core Mathematics

However you choose to enlarge your picture, your goal is to show that you multiplied each dimension by a fraction larger than 1. Compare your pictures with those of your classmates. Pay attention to how the fractions used affect the change in the size of the picture. When you are all finished, hang up and enjoy your pictures.

Question 4: How can you figure out servings of food?

Choose a food you might have in your pantry and read the label. Look for a food for which the serving size is a fraction, such as $\frac{1}{2}$ cup. If you prefer, you can use a recipe book instead.

Make a diagram that relates the amount of food in the package or recipe to the serving size. Show how to calculate the number of serving sizes in the package or recipe. Compare the information for several foods. You may be surprised to find out just how small a serving size might be or how many are in a package or recipe.

Share your results with the class. Compare what you found with the diagrams of other students.

Lesson 31 Converting Among Units of Measurement

5.MD.1 Convert among different-sized standard measurement units within a given measurement system (e.g., convert 5 cm to 0.05 m), and use these conversions in solving multi-step, real world problems.

Real World Connections

Toolbox

pencil
calculator

Key Word

convert

There are many times when you need to convert from one unit of measurement to another. Knowing different units of measurement and ways to change one unit to another can help you understand the quantities they describe.

Gianna drank four small bottles of water. Each bottle holds 230 milliliters of water. Did Gianna drink enough water if her coach wants her to drink 1 liter of water before her softball game? If not, how much more water does she need to drink?

To **convert**, or change, from one unit to another, you need to use the relationship between the units. For example, 1 ft equals 12 inches or 1 m equals 100 cm.

Multiply to convert from a larger unit to a smaller unit within the same system.	Divide to convert from a smaller unit to a larger unit within the same system.
Convert 9 ft to inches.	Convert 400 cm to meters.
1 ft = 12 in.	1 m = 100 cm
9 × 12 = 108 in.	400 ÷ 100 = 4 m
9 ft = 108 in.	400 cm = 4 m

Copying is illegal.

Take It Apart

To figure out how much water Gianna drank, follow some simple steps.

Step 1 Find the total amount she drank already.
    4 bottles × 230 mL/bottle = 920 mL

Step 2 Convert from milliliters to liters.
You are converting from a smaller unit to a larger unit.
You need to divide.
        1 L = 1,000 mL
        920 ÷ 1,000 = 0.92
So 920 mL = 0.92 L

Step 3 Compare. 0.92 < 1.
Gianna did not drink enough water.

Step 4 Subtract to find the difference.

1 L − 0.92 L = 0.08 L

She needs to drink 0.08 L more water.

Use the relationship between the units to convert each measurement and find the missing number.

1. 3 yd = _____ ft

2. 10 qt = _____ gal

3. _____ m = 50 cm

4. _____ mm = 34 cm

5. 2,000 m = _____ km

6. 6,500 g = _____ kg

7. 18 in. = _____ ft

8. _____ m = 8,000 mm

9. _____ oz = 1.25 lb

10. _____ m = 2 km

Put It Together

Use each description to convert from one unit of measurement to another.

1. Kaleigh ran 1 mile 45 feet. How many feet is that? _____

2. A truck is carrying 21/2ns. How many pounds is it carrying? _____

3. Jacob made a fruit punch with 16 pints of water. How many gallons of water did he use?

   _____

4. A length of border is 3 yards 1 foot long. How many inches long is it? _____

5. Tyler has a string that is 548 centimeters long. How many meters long is the string?

   _____

6. A scientist has 1,350 grams of salt for an experiment. How many kilograms of salt does the scientist have?

   _____

Answer the questions. Compare your answers with a classmate.

7. A box of pasta weighs 12 ounces. What is the weight, in pounds, of a case of 20 boxes of pasta?

   _____

8. Scott adds 12 mL of fertilizer to each of his five plants each day as part of his science project. How many liters of fertilizer will he need for 30 days?

   _____

9. A plant has grown 120 millimeters. How many more centimeters does it need to grow to be 1 meter tall?

   _____

10. Mrs. Hanson needs 2 cups of milk for each pie. How many gallons of milk does she need to make 10 pies?

   _____

Make It Work

Answer the questions below.

1. Pedro has a drink bottle that holds 125 mL. Sam has a drink bottle that holds 2 L. How much more does Sam's bottle hold than Pedro's?

   A. 875 mL   **B.** 1 L 75 mL

   C. 1 L 875 mL   **D.** 2 L 75 mL

2. Anita is making costumes for the cheerleading squad. She needs 25 cm of ribbon for each costume. If there are 18 cheerleaders, how many meters of ribbon should she buy?

   A. 4.5 m   **B.** 7.0 m

   C. 25 m   **D.** 43 m

3. A bridge can hold 15 tons. If each car averages 2,500 pounds, what is the maximum number of cars the bridge can hold at once? Show your work.

4. Mr. Harrison is putting a flexible fence around his garden. The fence is sold in 1-meter sections. How many sections will he need to use to completely surround the garden? Show your work.

   900 cm

   750 cm

5. Ms. Mason wants to give each student 150 mL of ocean water for a science investigation. There are 24 students in her class. If she has 4.0 L of ocean water, how many liters of ocean water will she have left over? Explain how you found the answer.

Lesson 32   Using Line Plots to Solve Problems Involving Measurement

5.MD.2   Make a line plot to display a data set of measurements in fractions of a unit $\left(\frac{1}{2}, \frac{1}{4}, \frac{1}{8}\right)$. Use operations on fractions for this grade to solve problems involving information presented in line plots. *For example, given different measurements of liquid in identical beakers, find the amount of liquid each beaker would contain if the total amount in all the beakers were redistributed equally.*

Real World Connections

One way to analyze and compare measurements is by using a line plot.

A **line plot** is a type of graph that shows the frequency of measurements along a number line. The graph below is a line plot.

Toolbox

pencil

ruler

Key Word

line plot

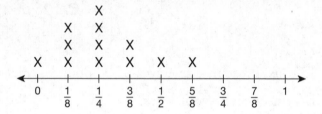

To make a line plot:

○ choose a scale that is appropriate for your data.

○ draw a horizontal line.

○ divide the line into equal parts based on your scale.

○ place an X over the number for each measurement.

Mrs. Riggs's class conducted an experiment that involved evaporating water. Each student was asked to measure the amount of water left in their containers after some evaporated. Their measurements are listed below. Make a line plot to display the measurements. Identify the amount of water most students had left.

$\frac{1}{4}$ c $\frac{3}{4}$ c $\frac{1}{2}$ c $\frac{1}{2}$ c $\frac{1}{2}$ c $\frac{1}{4}$ c $\frac{1}{4}$ c $\frac{3}{4}$ c $\frac{3}{4}$ c $\frac{1}{2}$ c $\frac{1}{4}$ c $\frac{1}{4}$ c $\frac{1}{2}$ c

$\frac{1}{2}$ c $\frac{3}{4}$ c $\frac{3}{4}$ c $\frac{1}{4}$ c $\frac{1}{2}$ c $\frac{1}{2}$ c $\frac{1}{2}$ c $\frac{3}{4}$ c $\frac{3}{4}$ c

---

Take It Apart

To plot the data, follow these steps.

Step 1 Choose a scale.
The measurements range from $\frac{1}{4}$ c to $\frac{3}{4}$ c.
An appropriate scale would range from 0 to 1 in intervals of $\frac{1}{4}$ c.

Step 2 Draw a number line.

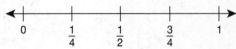

Step 3 Draw an X above the number for each measurement.

Step 4 Analyze the measurements.

The greatest number of Xs are above $\frac{1}{2}$.

More students have $\frac{1}{2}$ c of water remaining.

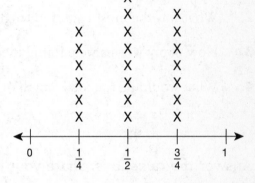

Analyze the line plot below. It shows the amount of rain, in inches, that several locations received in one week.

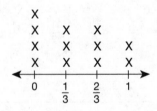

1. How many locations did not receive any rain? _____

2. How many locations received exactly 1 inch of rain? _____

3. How many locations were used to create the line plot? _____

4. If all the rain were combined and divided evenly
   among the locations, how much rain would each receive? _____

Put It Together

The line plot below shows the lengths of worms discovered by students during a nature walk. Analyze the line plot to answer each question.

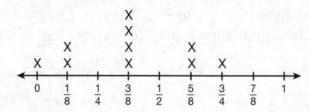

1. What is the length of the longest worm found? _____

2. What was the most common length of worms found? _____

3. How many worms were found in all? _____

4. What would be the total length of all the worms lined up end-to-end?

_____

Answer the questions. Share your ideas with a classmate.

5. Cindy is opening a gourmet chocolate shop. The data below show the price of each type of chocolate candy she sells in dollars. What scale should she use to represent the prices on a line plot? Explain your reason for the choice.

$\frac{1}{4}$ $\frac{3}{4}$ $\frac{3}{4}$ $\frac{1}{2}$ $\frac{1}{4}$ $\frac{1}{4}$ $\frac{1}{4}$ $\frac{1}{2}$ $\frac{1}{2}$ $\frac{1}{2}$ $\frac{1}{4}$ $\frac{1}{4}$ $\frac{3}{4}$ $\frac{3}{4}$ $\frac{3}{4}$

_____

_____

6. The line plot shows the number of ounces of medicine a veterinarian gave to each pet at an animal clinic. How much medicine did the veterinarian use for the 15 animals?

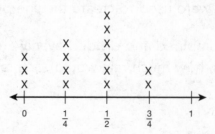

Make It Work

Answer the questions below.

Mauricio measured how much each plant in an experiment grew in one week. The line plot shows the growth of each plant in inches.

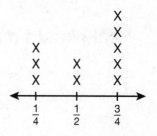

1. What is the range of the plant growth?

   A. $\frac{1}{4}$ in.   **B.** $\frac{1}{2}$ in.

   C. $\frac{3}{4}$ in.   **D.** 1 in.

2. What is the average plant growth?

   A. $\frac{3}{4}$ **B.** $\frac{1}{10}$

   C. $\frac{11}{20}$ **D.** $\frac{4}{22}$

3. Make a line plot to represent the data below.

   $\frac{1}{2}$ 3 $1\frac{1}{2}$ $\frac{1}{2}$ 2 $1\frac{1}{2}$ 2   2 $1\frac{1}{2}$ $\frac{1}{2}$ $1\frac{1}{2}$

4. A recycling company collects used paper. The line plot shows the fraction of a ton of paper collected from several different bins. If the recycling company pays $20 for each ton of paper collected, how much will the company pay for this collection? Round your answer to the nearest dollar.

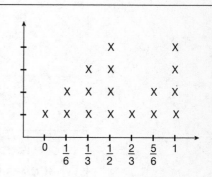

_____

_____

5. What is a line plot? How can you identify the most common data value (mode) from a line plot? How can you identify the range of data from a line plot? What does it mean if no Xs are written above a value on a line plot?

_____

_____

_____

5.MD.3.a A cube with side length 1 unit, called a "unit cube," is said to have "one cubic unit" of volume, and can be used to measure volume.

Real World Connections

Toolbox

pencil

Key Words

cube

unit cube

volume

There are all sorts of cubes—letter cubes, number cubes, paper cubes, and so on. You can use a special type of cube to learn about three-dimensional objects.

A **cube** is a three-dimensional object for which the length, height, and width are equal and its surface is made up of six squares. A **unit cube** is a cube for which all edges measure 1 unit. You can use a unit cube to measure the amount of space a solid figure takes up, or its **volume.**

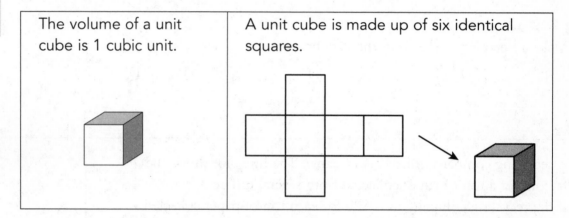

The volume of a unit cube is 1 cubic unit.

A unit cube is made up of six identical squares.

Tyrone is organizing a food collection by placing cans into boxes. What does he need to know to describe the volume of each box?

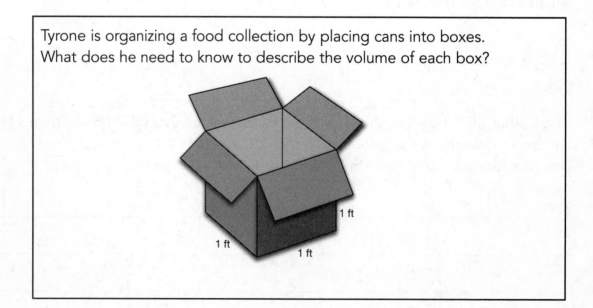

1 ft

1 ft

1 ft

Peoples Common Core Mathematics

 Take It Apart

To describe the volume of the box, follow some simple steps.

Step 1 Define volume.
Volume is the amount of space the box takes up.

Step 2 Think how to measure volume.
You can use a unit cube. The dimensions of a unit cube are 1 unit.
The box is a unit cube.

Step 3 Find and read the dimensions of the box.
Each edge is 1 ft.

The volume of the box is 1 cubic foot.

Use the steps above to write the volume of each cube.

1.
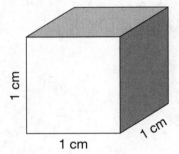

2.
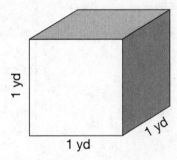

_____   _____

Put It Together

Use what you know about unit cubes to identify the figures that are unit cubes. Write "yes" next to the unit cubes. Write "no" next to the other figures.

1.

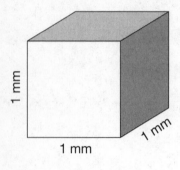

1 mm
1 mm
1 mm

_____

3.

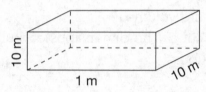

10 m
1 m
10 m

_____

2.

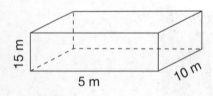

15 m
5 m
10 m

_____

4.

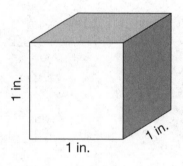

1 in.
1 in.
1 in.

_____

Answer the questions. Share your ideas with a classmate.

5. What information do you learn by knowing the volume of a box? Give an example of how this information might be helpful?

_____

_____

_____

6. Marci is mailing a box that has a volume of 1 cubic foot. Draw a picture of the box, and give its possible dimensions.

_____

Make It Work

Answer the questions below.

1. What is the side length of a unit cube?

   A. 0

   B. 1

   C. 2

   D. 4

2. How are unit cubes useful for describing solid figures?

   A. They can measure mass.

   B. They can measure temperature.

   C. They can measure weight.

   D. They can measure volume.

3. Charla is looking at a solid figure. How can she determine if it is a unit cube? What tool can she use to help her decide?

_____

_____

4. Jorge has several unit cubes. How can he use them to find the volume of an empty box?

_____

_____

_____

5. Kendall has a box of unit cubes. She stacks several of them together. How can she find the total volume of the stack of cubes? Give an example.

_____

_____

_____

Lesson 34 Using Unit Cubes to Measure Volume

5.MD.3.b   A solid figure which can be packed without gaps or overlaps using *n* unit cubes is said to have a volume of *n* cubic units.

Real World Connections

Toolbox

pencil

paper

Key Word

solid figure

In the previous lesson, you learned that unit cubes can be used to measure the volume of a solid figure. This relationship can be useful if you want to know how much you can fit into an object, like a box, or if you need to know how much space an object will take up.

A **solid figure** that can be packed without gaps or overlaps using *n* unit cubes is said to have a volume of *n* cubic units.

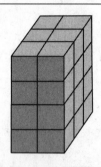

There are no spaces.

There are no gaps.

Count the cubes: 24 cubes

Volume = 24 cubic units

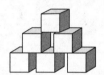

There are gaps between the cubes.

There are overlaps.

The figure is not a solid figure.

Each of the smaller cubes in the figure is one unit cube.
What is the volume of the box in cubic units?

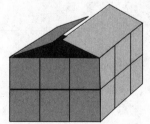

Take It Apart

To figure out the volume of the figure, follow some simple steps.

Step 1   Count the rows of the figure.

There are 2 rows.

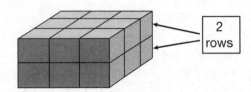

2
rows

Step 2   Count the unit cubes in each row.

There are 9 cubes in each row.

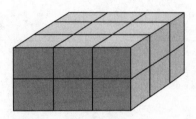

Step 3   Multiply the number of rows by the number of unit cubes.

2 rows × 9 unit cubes = 18 unit cubes

Step 4   Use the number of unit cubes to find the volume. There are no gaps or overlaps.
The volume is equal to the number of unit cubes.

The volume of the figure is 18 cubic units.

**Use the steps above to fill in the missing numbers describing the volume
of each figure made up of unit cubes.**

1.   3 rows, 8 cubes, —————— cubic units   4.   6 rows, 6 cubes, —————— cubic units

2.   2 rows, —————— cubes, 8 cubic units   5.   —————— row, 12 cubes, 12 cubic units

3.   —————— rows, 4 cubes, 16 cubic units   6.   6 rows, 8 cubes, —————— cubic units

Put It Together

Each cube shown is one unit cube. Write the volume of each figure.

1. _____

2. _____

3. _____

4. 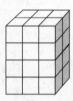 _____

Answer the questions. Share your ideas with a classmate.

5. Alison has a set of letter blocks. Each block is a unit cube. What is the volume of the figure she can build out of only vowels? What is the volume of the figure she can build out of all the letters?

_____

_____

6. You are making a solid figure from unit cubes. Draw three different figures you can build that each have a volume of 16 cubic units? (The figure will not have overlaps or gaps.)

_____

_____

Make It Work

Answer the questions below.

1. What is the volume of the figure?

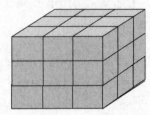

A. 9 cubic units   **B.** 11 cubic units

C. 18 cubic units   **D.** 27 cubic units

2. Which description matches a figure that has a volume of 24 cubic units?

A. 2 layers of 10 cubes

B. 4 layers of 6 cubes

C. 3 layers of 12 cubes

D. 6 layers of 3 cubes

3. Draw figures with each of the following volumes: 6 cubic units, 9 cubic units, 14 cubic units, and 20 cubic units.

_____

4. Pedro is building a tower out of unit cubes. The first floor of the tower is shown. He is going to add 3 more floors. What will be the total volume of the tower?

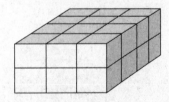

_____

5. A company packs number cubes into a box. The box can fit 36 number cubes without gaps or overlaps. List nine possible arrangements of number cubes in the box by describing the number of rows and the number of cubes in each row. Choose an arrangement that you think is most practical and explain why.

_____   _____   _____

_____   _____   _____

_____   _____   _____

_____

_____

5.MD.4   Measure volumes by counting unit cubes, using cubic cm, cubic in., cubic ft, and improvised units.

Real World Connections

You have been describing volume of unit cubes. You will often need to describe the volume of an object in specific units.

The volume of a unit cube is 1 cubic unit. You find the volume of a cube with specific units in much the same way. Keep in mind that volume is always measured in **cubic units**.

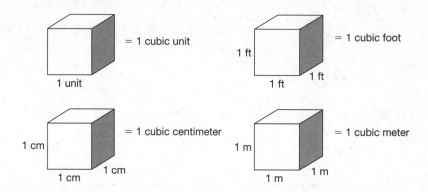

A candle company packs candles into boxes for shipment.
They use boxes like the one shown below in which each cube has a volume of 1 cubic in. What is the volume of the box?

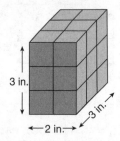

Take It Apart

To calculate the volume of the box, follow some simple steps.

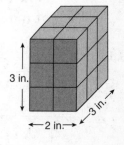

Step 1   Count the number of rows of cubes that make up the box.
There are 3 rows.

Step 2   Count the number of cubes in each row.
There are 6 cubes in each row.

Step 3   Multiply the number of rows by the number of cubes.
$3 \times 6 = 18$

Step 4   Use the unit of length to write the unit of volume.

Each length is measured in inches.
Volume should be measured in cubic inches.

The volume of the box is 18 cubic inches.

Use the steps above to write the units of volume for each box.

1.
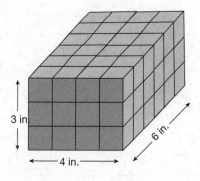

2.
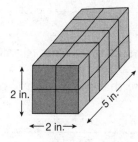

_____

_____

3.
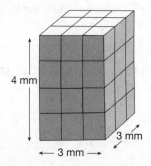

4.
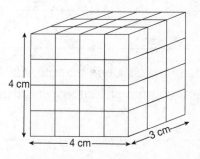

_____

_____

Put It Together

Find the volume of each figure. Be sure to include the correct units of measurement.

1.

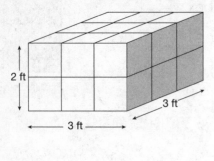

2 ft

3 ft

3 ft

_____

2.

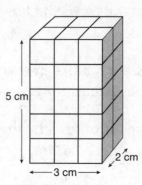

5 cm

2 cm

3 cm

_____

3.

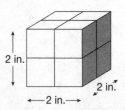

2 in.

2 in.

2 in.

_____

4.

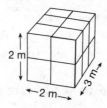

2 m

3 m

2 m

_____

Answer the questions. Share your ideas with a classmate.

5. Draw a solid figure that has a volume of 18 cubic inches. Explain how you chose the shape you did.

_____

_____

6. How many cubic feet are in a cubic yard? Draw a diagram to show the answer.

_____

_____

7. A company makes a box that measures 1 m by 1 m by 1 m. How many cubes will fit in the box if each cube has a volume of 1 cubic centimeter?

_____

Make It Work

Answer the questions below.

1. Each cube in the figure below has a volume of 1 cubic centimeter. What is the volume of the figure?

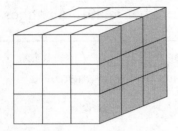

A. 3 cubic centimeters

B. 9 cubic centimeters

C. 18 cubic centimeters

D. 27 cubic centimeters

2. If the volume of the figure is 24 cubic feet, what is the volume of each cube in the diagram?

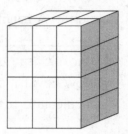

A. 1 cubic foot

B. 2 cubic feet

C. 4 cubic feet

D. 6 cubic feet

3. The shape below is made up of cubes. What are the dimensions of the figure? What is the volume of each cube? What is the volume of the entire figure?

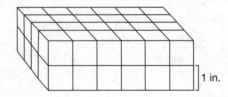

1 in.

_____

_____

4. Diana works for a shipping company. They have boxes of all different sizes. How can several boxes with different shapes have the same volume? Draw an example. Tell why this might be useful.

_____

_____

_____

Lesson 36 Finding a Formula to Calculate the Volume of a Rectangular Prism

5.MD.5.a Find the volume of a right rectangular prism with whole-number side lengths by packing it with unit cubes, and show that the volume is the same as would be found by multiplying the edge lengths, equivalently by multiplying the height by the area of the base. Represent threefold whole-number products as volumes, e.g., to represent the associative property of multiplication.

Real World Connections

Toolbox

pencil

Key Word

formula

It is not always convenient to find volume by counting unit cubes. You can use what you know about unit cubes to find a formula for calculating volume. A **formula** is a mathematical statement that relates quantities.

Heidi's class built this structure from blocks for a play. They need to know how much space it will take up. How can they find a formula to calculate the volume of the figure?

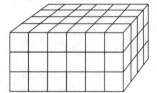

You have been using different methods to count the number of cubes in a solid figure. You can count individual cubes, or use multiplication.

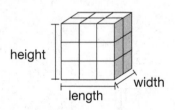

Length = 3 unit cubes

Width = 2 unit cubes

Height = 3 unit cubes

You can find the total number of unit cubes by multiplying the length by the width by the height

Volume (V) = length (l) × width (w) × height (h)

$= l \times w \times h$

$= 3 \text{ units} \times 2 \text{ units} \times 3 \text{ units} = 18 \text{ cubic units}$

Because you multiply the same unit three times, another way to write the unit for volume is as a cube. $V = 18 \text{ units}^3$

Take It Apart

To figure out the volume of the figure, follow some simple steps.

Step 1 List the dimensions of the figure.

Length = 6 unit cubes
Width = 4 unit cubes
Height = 3 unit cubes

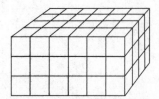

Step 2 Write the formula for finding the volume of a figure.

$V = l \times w \times h$

Step 3 Replace the letters in the formula with the dimensions of the figure.

$V = l \times w \times h$

$V = 6 \times 4 \times 3 = 72$ cubic units

The volume of the figure is 72 cubic units.

Use the steps above to complete each formula for the volume of the figure.

1.

$V = 2 \times \underline{} \times \underline{}$

2.

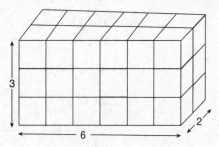

$V = \underline{} \times 2 \times \underline{}$

3.

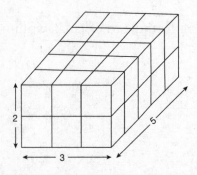

$V = \underline{} \times \underline{} \times 2$

4.

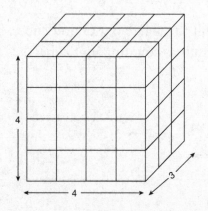

$V = 4 \times \underline{} \times \underline{}$

Put It Together

Use what you know to write an equation to find each volume.

1.

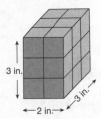

3 in.
3 in.
2 in.

V = _____

2.

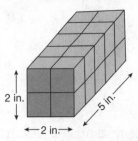

2 in.
5 in.
2 in.

V = _____

3.

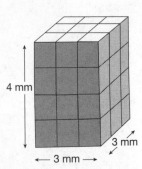

4 mm
3 mm
3 mm

V = _____

4.

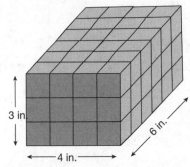

3 in.
6 in.
4 in.

V = _____

Answer the questions. Compare your results with a classmate.

5. Each cube has a volume of 1 cm³. What is the volume of the entire figure? Show your work.

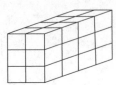

_____

_____

6. Claudia built this figure out of unit cubes. Show that using a formula to calculate volume produces the same result as counting unit cubes.

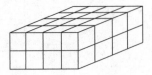

_____

_____

Make It Work

Answer the questions below.

1. Which formula can be used to find the volume of the figure below?

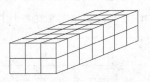

A. $V = l + w + h$ **B.** $V = l^3$

C. $V = l \times w \times h$ **D.** $V = 3l$

2. Which equation can be used to find the volume of the figure below?

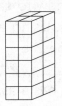

A. $V = 2 \times 2 \times 6$ **B.** $V = 2 + 2 + 6$

C. $V = 23$ **D.** $V = 226$

3. Why can't you use the volume formula to find the volume of the figure below? How can you find its volume?

_____

_____

_____

_____

4. The formula you have been using is for finding the volume of a rectangular prism. Simplify the formula for a cube.

_____

_____

5. The area of the base of the figure in question 2 is $l \times w$. Rewrite the formula for the volume of a rectangular prism in terms of the area of the base, b.

_____

Lesson 37 Using Formulas to Find the Volume of a Rectangular Prism

5.MD.5.b Apply the formulas $V = l \times w \times h$ and $V = b \times h$ for rectangular prisms to find volumes of right rectangular prisms with whole-number edge lengths in the context of solving real world and mathematical problems.

Real World Connections

Toolbox

pencil

calculator

Key Word

rectangular prism

You need to know how to calculate volume from formulas to find the volume of everyday objects. Using a formula is much more practical than filling every object with unit cubes!

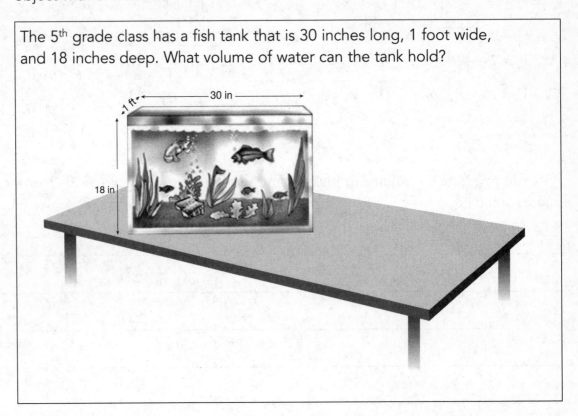

The 5ᵗʰ grade class has a fish tank that is 30 inches long, 1 foot wide, and 18 inches deep. What volume of water can the tank hold?

The fish tank is a rectangular prism. Remember that a **rectangular prism** is a three-dimensional figure whose surface is made up of 6 rectangles.

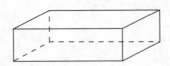

To find the volume of a rectangular prism, use either formula for volume.

$V = l \times w \times h$

$V = 2 \text{ cm} \times 3 \text{ cm} \times 4 \text{ cm} = 24 \text{ cm}^3$

$b = 2 \text{ cm} \times 3 \text{ cm} = 6 \text{ cm}^2$

$V = b \times h$

$V = 6 \text{ cm}^2 \times 4 \text{ cm} = 24 \text{ cm}^3$

Take It Apart

To find the volume of the fish tank, follow some simple steps.

Step 1 Convert all measurements to the same unit.
You can choose either inches or feet. For this example,
you can choose inches to keep the numbers whole.

length = 30 in.
width = 1 ft = 12 in.
height = 18 in.

Step 2 Choose a formula for volume.
$V = l \times w \times h$

Step 3 Substitute the given measurements into the formula and solve.
$V = 30$ in. $\times 12$ in. $\times 18$ in. $= 6{,}480$ in.^{3}

The tank can hold 6,480 in.^{3} of water. (That's almost 30 gallons!)

**Use the strategy above to find volume given the dimensions
of a rectangular prism.**

1. $l = 10$ cm, $w = 4$ cm, $h = 2$ cm
   $V =$ _____

2. $l = 5$ m, $w = 2$ m, $h = 6$ m
   $V =$ _____

3. $l = 4$ ft, $w = 6$ ft, $h = 3$ ft
   $V =$ _____

4. $l = 1$ yd, $w = 4$ yd, $h = 9$ yd
   $V =$ _____

5. $l = 8$ in., $w = 3$ in., $h = 1$ in.
   $V =$ _____

6. $l = 6$ mm, $w = 10$ mm, $h = 2$ mm
   $V =$ _____

Put It Together

Use what you know about volume to answer each question.

1. What is the volume of the book?

_____

2. What is the volume of the carton?

_____

3. What volume can the wagon hold?

_____

4. What is the volume of the cabin?

_____

Answer the questions. Share your ideas with a classmate.

5. A builder is planning a swimming pool to be 15 feet wide, 20 feet long, and 6 feet deep. By how much will the volume of the swimming pool increase if the depth becomes 10 feet?

_____

_____

6. A toy bin is 2 feet wide and 2 ft deep. If the volume of the toy bin is 12 ft^3, how long is it?

_____

Make It Work

Answer the questions below.

1. The planter outside the museum has a volume of 40 m³. If the planter is 5 m long and 4 m wide, how deep is it?

   A. 2 m

   B. 4 m

   C. 9 m

   D. 20 m

2. Mrs. Winslow is selecting a cabinet for her classroom. Which dimensions describe the cabinet with the greatest volume?

   A. 2 ft long, 2 ft wide, 4 ft tall

   B. 3 ft long, 2 ft wide, 4 ft tall

   C. 3 ft long, 1 ft wide, 5 ft tall

   D. 1 ft long, 2 ft wide, 6 ft tall

3. Gretchen is bringing rice treats to school. She cut each treat into a rectangular prism that measures 3 in. × 2 in. × 1 in. If she has 30 treats, what is the volume of the box she needs to carry them in if she wants to keep them in one layer?

   _____

   _____

5. What happens to volume when the dimensions of a rectangular prism are doubled? Create a data table to support your answer.

5.MD.5.c   Recognize volume as additive. Find volumes of solid figures composed of two non-overlapping right rectangular prisms by adding the volumes of the non-overlapping parts, applying this technique to solve real world problems.

Real World Connections

Toolbox

pencil

Key Word

complex figure

Real-world objects are not always rectangular prisms. Different kinds of shapes can make it more challenging to find volume. Fortunately, if you remember how to find the volume of a rectangular prism, you can often divide a figure into smaller parts so you can find the volume.

> Pizza Mania uses boxes that are 20 inches long, 20 inches wide, and 2 inches deep for their pizzas. Giuseppe piled 15 pizza boxes on top of each other. How much space does the pile of pizza boxes take up?

Some solid figures are made up of combinations of rectangular prisms. These figures are sometimes known as **complex figures**. Remember that you began studying volume by considering figures made of unit cubes. Each unit cube is a rectangular prism. You added the volume of each cube to find the total volume of the figure.

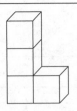

The volume of each rectangular prism is 1 cm^3.

There are 4 rectangular prisms.

1 cm^3 + 1 cm^3 + 1 cm^3 + 1 cm^3 = 4 cm^3

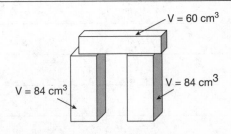

If you can divide a figure into rectangular prisms, you can find the sum of the volumes of individual prisms.

60 cm^3 + 84 cm^3 + 84 cm^3 = 228 cm^3

Take It Apart

To find the volume of the pile of pizza boxes, follow some simple steps.

Step 1 Divide the figure into rectangular prisms.
Each pizza box is a rectangular prism.
There are 15 rectangular prisms.

Step 2 Find the volume of each rectangular prism.
Each pizza box has the same volume.
$V = 20$ in. $\times$ 20 in. $\times$ 2 in. $= 800$ in.^{3}

Step 3 Add the volumes together.
Because all of the volumes are the same, you need to use repeated addition.
Repeated addition is the same as multiplication.
15×800 in.$^3 = 12,000$ in.^{3}

The total volume of the pile of pizza boxes is 12,000 in.^{3}.

**Use the strategy above to write an expression for the volume of each figure.
You do not need to calculate the total volume.**

1.

$V = 36$ cm^3

$V = 336$ cm^3

_____

2.

$V = 8$ in.^{3}

$V = 36$ in.^{3}

$V = 112$ in.^{3}

_____

3.

$V = 16$ in.^{3}

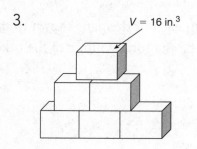

_____

_____

4.

$V = 96$ mm^3

$V = 96$ mm^3

$V = 96$ mm^3

$V :$

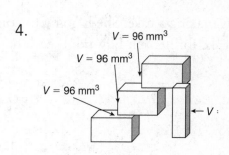

_____

Put It Together

Find the volume of each figure. Be sure to include the correct units of measurement.

1.

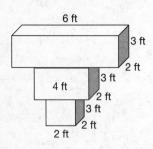

2.

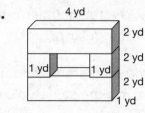

_____   _____

Answer the questions. Compare your ideas with a classmate.

3. A shoebox is 9 inches long, 6 inches wide, and 4 inches tall. A clerk stacks shoeboxes in 5 rows with 10 boxes in each row. What is the total volume the shoe boxes take up?

_____

_____

4. Jonathon makes a walkway out of bricks. He uses 20 bricks that are 30 inches long, 20 inches wide, and 2 inches thick. He uses 10 bricks that are 15 inches long, 10 inches wide, and 2 inches thick. What is the total volume of the walkway?

_____

_____

5. Anisha is making a cake. She is going to combine the cakes from each of the pans shown to make a letter E cake for her son Edward. If each pan is filled, what will be the total volume of the cake?

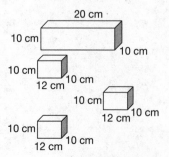

_____

Make It Work

Answer the questions below.

1. Buddy made a wedding cake with three levels. What is the total volume of the cake?

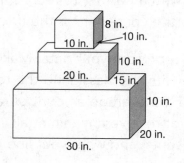

   A. 9,800 in.³   **B.** 6,000 in.³

   C. 2,400 in.³   **D.** 800 in.³

2. Margareta made this figure as part of a model. What is the volume of the figure?

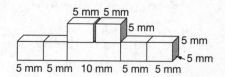

   A. 500 mm³   **B.** 1,250 mm³

   C. 1,000 mm³   **D.** 3,000 mm³

3. Three cubes are stacked on top of each other. Their total height is 18 inches. What is the volume of the stack of cubes?

_____

_____

4. The volume of the shaded section of the cube is 4 m³. The height of the shaded section is 1 m. If the total height of the cube is 2 m, explain how to find the total volume of the cube.

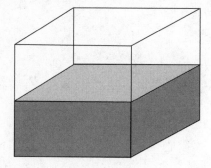

_____

_____

_____

Kick It Up!

Question 1: How can you collect and display weather data?

You see and hear weather data all the time. Now you can collect some for yourself. Use a rain gauge, graduated cylinder, beaker, or other container to collect rain. Each day for one month, work with a partner to record the amount of water in the container. Then empty the container for the next day.

At the end of the month, create a line plot to represent your data. Make your line plot into a poster that you can share with the class. Find the total amount of rain that fell during the month, and the average amount of rain each day. Keep in mind that some days may not receive any rain at all. Explain what each mark on the line plot represents, and what your line plot shows.

Question 2: How are unit cubes useful for measuring volume?

Find or make a unit cube out of materials you find in your classroom or home. For example, you might fold construction paper into a cube or you might have an object in the shape of a unit cube. Then obtain one or more empty boxes. Make a video, picture album, or journal showing how you can use the cubes to find the volume of the box. Prove that using the cubes yields the same results as using the formula for the volume of a rectangular prism.

Chapter 4

Question 3: Can different figures have the same volume?

Obtain a set of cube blocks. Work with a small group to make as many rectangular prisms as you can with the same volume. For example, you can make seven different rectangular prisms that have a volume of 64 cubic units. Draw a picture or take a photo of each prism. Make a diagram or poster that shows how you found the volume of each figure, and indicates that they are the same.

If time allows, compete with other groups to find the greatest number of combinations of shapes. You may need to combine with other groups to increase the number of available cubes.

You can expand the activity by including other shapes that are not rectangular prisms. When you do this, the possible combinations increase tremendously. Use your imagination and get building.

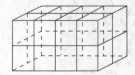

Question 4: How much space do everyday objects take up?

Locate common objects in your school or home that are in the shape of rectangular prisms or combinations of rectangular prisms. For example, your refrigerator might be a rectangular prism. A photocopier on a stand might be a combination of rectangular prisms. Measure the dimensions of each object you choose. Then draw a diagram of the object, its dimensions, and its volume. Compare the objects you chose with those of your classmates.

Lesson 39 Plotting and Naming Points on a Coordinate System

5.G.1 Use a pair of perpendicular number lines, called axes, to define a coordinate system, with the intersection of the lines (the origin) arranged to coincide with the 0 on each line and a given point in the plane located by using an ordered pair of numbers, called its coordinates. Understand that the first number indicates how far to travel from the origin in the direction of one axis, and the second number indicates how far to travel in the direction of the second axis, with the convention that the names of the two axes and the coordinates correspond (e.g., *x*-axis and *x*-coordinate, *y*-axis and *y*-coordinate).

Real World Connections

Key Words

coordinate
 system
axes
origin
ordered pair

It is helpful to locate and plot points on a coordinate grid. This lets you see how the points are arranged and how far one point is from another.

Jaime's teacher wrote coordinates on the blackboard. Where should Jaime plot the point on a coordinate grid?

A **coordinate system** is made up of perpendicular number lines called **axes**. The horizontal number line is the *x*-axis and the vertical number line is the *y*-axis. The axes meet at the 0 on each line to form the **origin**. The system is also described as a coordinate plane or a coordinate grid.

Any given point is located by using an **ordered pair**. The first number in the ordered pair indicates how far to travel on the *x*-axis. The second number indicates how far to travel up the *y*-axis.
(*x*-coordinate, *y*-coordinate).

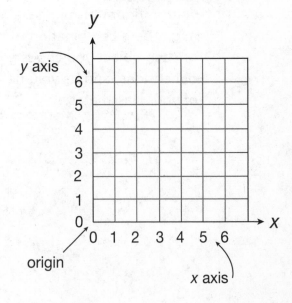

Coordinate Grid

Take It Apart

Use a strategy similar to this one to plot (5, 3) on a coordinate grid.

Step 1 Identify the coordinates:
(*x*-coordinate, *y*-coordinate)
x-coordinate: 5
y-coordinate: 3

Step 2 Plot the *x*-coordinate.
Start at the origin.
Move to the right 5 units.

Step 3 Plot the *y*-coordinate.
Move up 3 units.

Step 4 Draw and label the point.

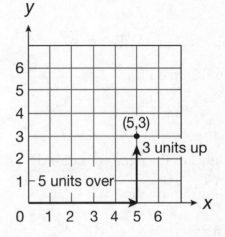

Use the strategy above to plot the points listed below.

(3, 4)   (9, 0)   (5, 5)

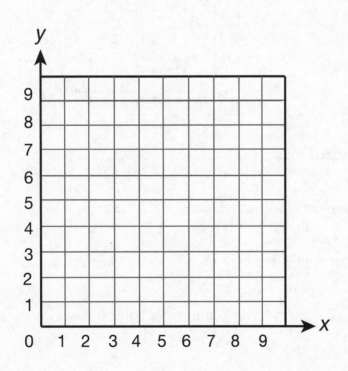

Put It Together

Use what you know about coordinates to complete each description.

1. (5, 9)

5 units to the right on the *x*-axis

———— units up on the ————————

2. (————, ————)

6 units to the right on the *x*-axis

1 unit up on the *y*-axis

3. (3, 0)

———— units to the right on the *x*-axis

———— units up on the *y*-axis

4. (————, ————)

2 units to the right on the *x*-axis

9 units up on the *y*-axis

Use the coordinate grid to answer each question.

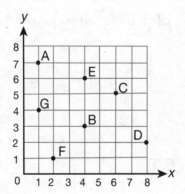

5. Which point is located at (6, 5)? ————————————

6. What are the coordinates of Point *A*? ————————————

7. Which point is over 4 units and up 3 units from the origin? ————————————

8. Which point is up 2 units and over 2 units from Point *B*? ————————————

Make It Work

Answer the questions below.

1. What are the coordinates of Point *C*?

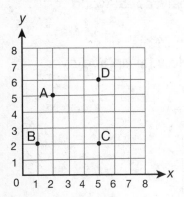

A. (2, 5)	**B.** (1, 2)
C. (5, 2)	**D.** (5, 6)

2. Which ordered pair will be the fourth corner of the square *ABCD*?

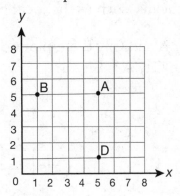

A. (5, 5)	**B.** (5, 6)
C. (1, 1)	**D.** (5, 1)

3.

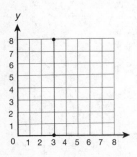

Tyler was asked to plot (8, 3) on a coordinate plane. His point is shown. Did he plot the point correctly? If not, what error did he make?

_____

4. Vanessa plotted (2, 1) and (2, 5) on a coordinate plane. Give the coordinates for two other points that would form a rectangle. Explain how you found your answer.

_____

_____

Lesson 40 Solving Problems by Graphing and Naming Points

5.G.2 Represent real world and mathematical problems by graphing points in the first quadrant of the coordinate plane, and interpret coordinate values of points in the context of the situation.

Real World Connections

You can use ordered pairs on a coordinate plane to analyze real-world problems, such as the locations of cities.

City A and City B are plotted on a coordinate plane. How far up and over from City A is City B?

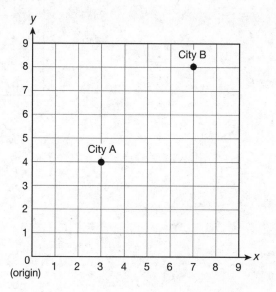

A point on a coordinate plane can represent a real-world object, such as a location, building, or item. Plotting objects can help you see how they are arranged or how close together they are.

The coordinate plane shows the locations of home, school, and the soccer field. You can see that the soccer field is up and to the left of home. School is up and to the right.

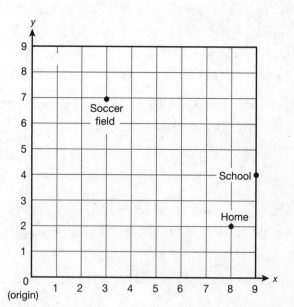

Take It Apart

Use a strategy similar to the one above to compare the locations of City A and City B on the coordinate plane.

Step 1 Find the coordinates of City A.
x-coordinate: 3
y-coordinate: 4
(3, 4)

Step 2 Find the coordinates of City B.
x-coordinate: 7
y-coordinate: 8
(7, 8)

Step 3 Find the difference between the x-coordinates.
7 − 3 = 4
City B is over 4 units.

Step 4 Find the difference between the y-coordinates.
8 − 4 = 4
City B is up 4 units.

City B is up 4 units and over 4 units from City A.

Use the strategy above to compare the groups plotted on this coordinate plane.

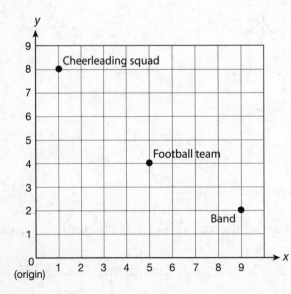

1. What point describes the location of the cheerleading squad?

   _____

2. Describe a path from the cheerleading squad to the band. Possible answer:

   _____

3. If the football coach is 2 units up and 3 units to the right of the football team, what point describes the coach's position?

   _____

Lesson 40 Solving Problems by Graphing and Naming Points

Put It Together

Use what you know about coordinate planes to answer each question.

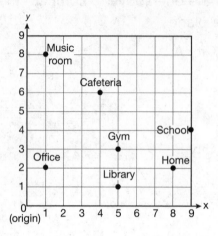

1. Which school area is located at (4, 6)?

_____

2. Describe a path from the library to the office?

_____

_____

Lakes are located at each point on the coordinate plane. Answer the questions using the graph.

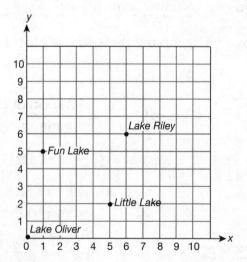

3. What name describes the location of Lake Oliver?   _____

4. Each unit on the coordinate grid is 8 miles. What is the shortest distance from Fun Lake to Lake Riley?

_____

Make It Work

Answer the questions below.

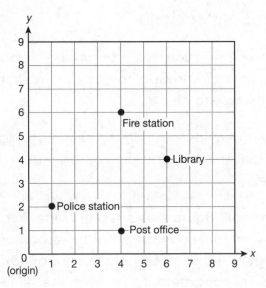

1. Which city building is located at (4, 6)?

    A. post office   B. library

    C. fire station   D. police station

2. Which describes a path from the post office to the library?

    A. up 3 and over 2   B. up 1 and over 3

    C. up 5 and over 0   D. up 2 and over 3

3. The attractions at a water park are plotted on a coordinate plane. The Frantic Fountain is at (3, 2). The Wacky Water Slide is up 4 units and right 8 units from the Frantic Fountain. What are the coordinates of the water slide?

   _____

5. You have been asked to plot the parts of a recreation complex on a coordinate plane. Show the following points:

   skateboard park (1, 7)

   baseball field (3, 3)

   basketball courts (6, 5)

   swimming pool (7, 1)

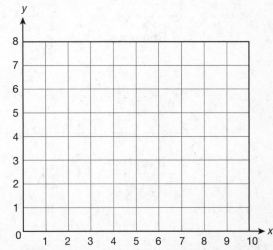

Lesson 41 Classifying Quadrilaterals

5.G.3 Understand that attributes belonging to a category of two-dimensional figures also belong to all subcategories of that category. *For example, all rectangles have four right angles and squares are rectangles, so all squares have four right angles.*

Real World Connections

Key Words

two-dimensional
figure

polygon

quadrilateral

congruent

Your soccer coach tells your team to run the shape of a rectangle. Easy enough, or is it? Knowing how to classify shapes can help you decide the best way to run.

A soccer player decides to run in the shape of a square. How can you decide if the player is meeting the coach's requirement to run in the shape of a rectangle?

A **two-dimensional figure** exists in one plane. In other words, it is flat. A two-dimensional shape made up of three or more line segments is called a **polygon.** A four-sided polygon is a **quadrilateral.** Two or more quadrilaterals are **congruent** if they have the same size and shape, and all their related parts are also congruent. The diagram below summarizes the features of common quadrilaterals. They are marked to show congruent sides and angles.

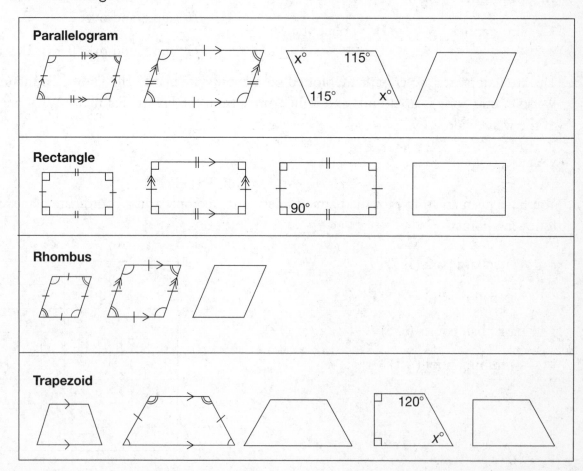

Copying is illegal.

Take It Apart

Use a strategy similar to this one to decide if a square is a rectangle.

Step 1 List the properties of a rectangle.
4 sides
4 right angles
opposite sides are parallel and congruent

Step 2 List the properties of a square.
4 sides
4 right angles
opposite sides are parallel
all sides are congruent

Rectangle   Square

Step 3 Find the difference between the two shapes.
All of the sides of a square are congruent.
All sides of a rectangle do not have to be congruent.

Step 4 Classify a square.
A square is also a rectangle.

The soccer player is meeting the coach's requirement.

Use the strategy above to complete each sentence using one of the terms provided.

always   sometimes   never

1. A quadrilateral is _____
   a rhombus.

2. A hexagon is _____
   a quadrilateral.

3. A rectangle is _____
   a quadrilateral.

4. A kite is _____
   a rhombus.

5. A rectangle is _____
   a parallelogram.

6. A square is _____
   a parallelogram.

Put It Together

Use what you know about quadrilaterals to list all the names that describe each shape. Choose from the following names, and indicate if no names apply.

quadrilateral, parallelogram, rectangle, square, rhombus, trapezoid

1.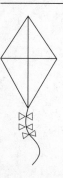

_____

2.

_____

3.

4.

_____

_____

5.

_____

Classify each quadrilateral. Write "yes" in each column that is a name for the shape. Keep in mind that some shapes have more than one name.

	Parallelogram	Rectangle	Rhombus	Square	Trapezoid
6.					
7.					
8.					
9.					

 Peoples Common Core Mathematics

Make It Work

Answer the questions below.

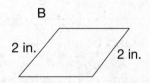

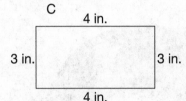
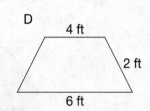

1. Which of these shapes can be classified as a parallelogram, rectangle, square, and rhombus?

   A. Shape A   **B.** Shape C

   C. Shape B   **D.** Shape D

2. Which of these shapes can be classified as a trapezoid?

   A. Shape A   **B.** Shape C

   C. Shape B   **D.** Shape D

3. What are five possible names for a four-sided shape with opposite sides that are parallel and all sides of the same length?

_____

4. Which quadrilaterals have only right angles? _____

5. Draw a Venn diagram that shows the relationships among quadrilaterals. Include parallelograms, rectangles, squares, rhombuses, and trapezoids.

Venn Diagram

Lesson 42 Describing Two-Dimensional Figures

5.G.4   Classify two-dimensional figures in a hierarchy based on properties.

Real World Connections

Artists and architects design artwork, buildings, and other structures. They incorporate a variety of two-dimensional figures in their structures. It is helpful to know the properties of two-dimensional figures to describe their work and other real-life objects.

What two-dimensional figures can you see in this design from ancient Pompeii in modern-day Italy?

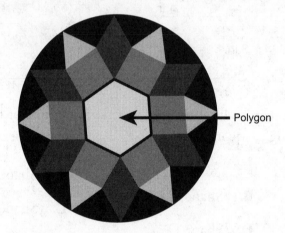

Polygon

Polygons are named by the number of sides they have. The table below shows some common polygons.

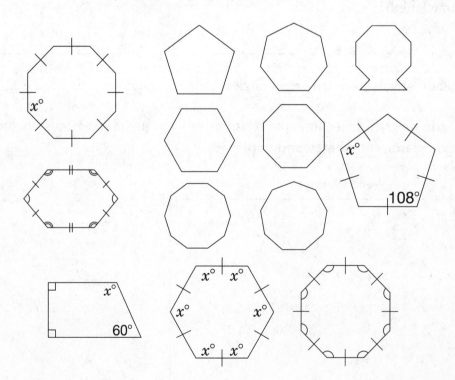

Take It Apart

Use a strategy similar to this one to identify polygons in common objects.

Step 1 Look for closed shapes with sides made up of line segments.

Step 2 Count the number of sides for each shape. Use the number of sides to name each polygon.

The artwork has triangles, quadrilaterals, and a hexagon.

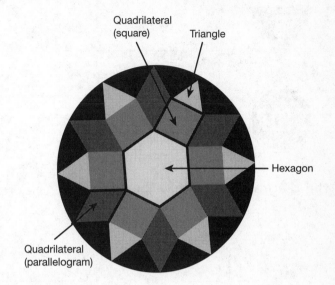

Quadrilateral (square)   Triangle

Hexagon

Quadrilateral (parallelogram)

Use the strategy above to name each shape described.

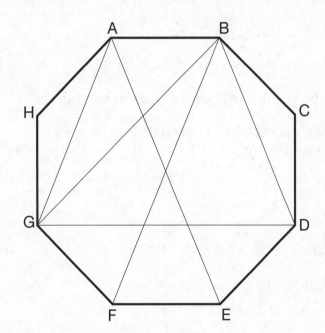

1. *ABCDEFGH* = _____

2. *ABCDGH* = _____

3. *BDG* = _____

4. *DEFG* = _____

5. *ABCDG* = _____

6. *AEFG* = _____

Put It Together

Use what you know about polygons to name each street sign.

1. _____

2. _____

3. _____

4. _____

Use the diagram to identify the triangles.

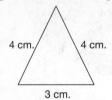

4 cm.   4 cm.

3 cm.

Isosceles Triangle

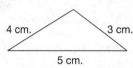

4 cm.   3 cm.

5 cm.

Scalene Triangle

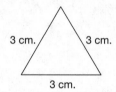

3 cm.   3 cm.

3 cm.

Equilateral Triangle

5. Based on the diagram, name each type of triangle.

_____ a triangle that has two congruent sides

_____ a triangle that does not have any congruent sides

_____ a triangle that has three congruent sides

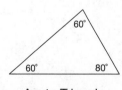

90°

Right Triangle

60°

60°   80°

Acute Triangle

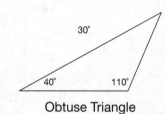

30°

40°   110°

Obtuse Triangle

6. Based on the diagram, define each type of triangle.

right: _____

acute: _____

obtuse: _____

7. How is an obtuse isosceles triangle like an acute isosceles triangle? How are they different?

_____

_____

Make It Work

Answer the questions below.

1. Tasha drew a figure that has 6 sides and 6 angles. Which figure did she draw?

A. hexagon   **B.** pentagon

C. triangle   **D.** octagon

2. Hector has a rug that has 5 sides and 5 angles. What shape describes Hector's rug?

A. quadrilateral   **B.** octagon

C. triangle   **D.** pentagon

3. Based on the diagram, how would you define a regular polygon?

_____

_____

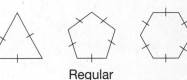

Regular

Non-Regular

4. Describe a pattern that describes the sum of the angles of a polygon.

_____

_____

_____

Polygon	Number of Sides	Sum of Angles
Triangle	3	180°
Quadrilateral	4	360°
Pentagon	5	540°

5. Diagonal lines can be drawn from one vertex of a polygon to the others to form triangles. Complete the chart to describe the polygon, the number of sides, the number of angles, and the number of triangles that can be formed.

Polygon	Number of Sides	Number of Angles	Number of Triangles
Quadrilateral		4	
	5		3
		6	

What is the pattern in the relationship between the number of sides and the number of triangles formed?

_____

_____

Based on the pattern, how many triangles would you expect to be formed from an octagon? _____

Question 1: What steps do you follow to plot a point on a coordinate plane?

One way to make sure you understand a concept is to teach it to someone else. Think about the steps you follow to plot a point. Now make the steps into a short film by drawing a series of pictures that show how to plot a specific point on a coordinate plane. Arrange your pictures as if they were frames in a movie reel. Then show your movie to the class.

Question 2: How can you describe your school using a coordinate plane?

You might tell a new student to go down the hall and to the left to get to a classroom. Another way to share the information is to use a coordinate plane. Work with a group to make a coordinate plane that shows at least five places in your school. Begin by measuring out the locations and drawing a sketch. Then use your sketch to show the locations on a grid. When you are finished, show the class how you can use the grid to get from one location to another.

Question 3: How can you name the same thing in different ways?

If someone asked where you live, you probably would be more specific than giving the name of the country. You might tell your state, city, or even your neighborhood. In the same way, you can describe quadrilaterals with general names and specific names that give more information about them. Work with a partner to make a model that shows why a particular figure has more than one name. For example, you might show why a square has so many names.

You might use paper fasteners to attach edges made of cardboard and show how you can change one figure into another. You might make different models to represent each figure. Use your imagination and be creative. Demonstrate your model for the class.

 Question 4: Where can you find two-dimensional figures?

Did you know you are surrounded by two-dimensional figures? Look around and you will see. For example, the outside of your refrigerator door might be a rectangle or the top of your kitchen table might be an octagon.

Look for as many examples as you can find around your home or school. Take a photograph or draw a picture of the objects. Highlight and label the figure. Make a poster showing all the examples you found.

Points	Criteria
	Rubric for Evaluating Math Assignments
4	A 4-point response shows a thorough understanding of the essential mathematical concepts of the problem. The student executes procedures correctly and gives relevant responses to all parts of the task. The response contains a clear, effective explanation detailing how the problem was solved and why decisions were made. The response contains few minor errors, if any.
3	A 3-point response shows a nearly complete understanding of the problem's essential mathematical concepts. The student executes nearly all procedures and gives relevant responses to most parts of the task. The response may contain a correct numerical answer, but the required work is not provided or the response may contain minor errors.
2	A 2-point response shows limited understanding of the essential mathematical concepts of the problem. The response and procedures may be incomplete and/or may contain major errors. The explanation of how the problem was solved and why decisions were made may be confusing.
1	A 1-point response shows insufficient understanding of the problem's essential mathematical concepts. The procedures, if any, contain major errors. There may be no explanation of the solution or the reader is unable to understand how and why decisions were made.
0	A 0-point response is irrelevant, illegible, incomprehensible, or shows that no legitimate attempt was made to solve the problem.

TABLE 1. Common addition and subtraction situations.[6]

	Result Unknown	Change Unknown	Start Unknown
Add to	Two bunnies sat on the grass. Three more bunnies hopped there. How many bunnies are on the grass now? $2 + 3 = ?$	Two bunnies were sitting on the grass. Some more bunnies hopped there. Then there were five bunnies. How many bunnies hopped over to the first two? $2 + ? = 5$	Some bunnies were sitting on the grass. Three more bunnies hopped there. Then there were five bunnies. How many bunnies were on the grass before? $? + 3 = 5$
Take from	Five apples were on the table. I ate two apples. How many apples are on the table now? $5 - 2 = ?$	Five apples were on the table. I ate some apples. Then there were three apples. How many apples did I eat? $5 - ? = 3$	Some apples were on the table. I ate two apples. Then there were three apples. How many apples were on the table before? $? - 2 = 3$

	Total Unknown	Addend Unknown	Both Addends Unknown[1]
Put Together/ Take Apart[2]	Three red apples and two green apples are on the table. How many apples are on the table? $3 + 2 = ?$	Five apples are on the table. Three are red and the rest are green. How many apples are green? $3 + ? = 5$, $5 - 3 = ?$	Grandma has five flowers. How many can she put in her red vase and how many in her blue vase? $5 = 0 + 5, 5 = 5 + 0$ $5 = 1 + 4, 5 = 4 + 1$ $5 = 2 + 3, 5 = 3 + 2$

	Difference Unknown	Bigger Unknown	Smaller Unknown
Compare[3]	("How many more?" version): Lucy has two apples. Julie has five apples. How many more apples does Julie have than Lucy? ("How many fewer?" version): Lucy has two apples. Julie has five apples. How many fewer apples does Lucy have than Julie? $2 + ? = 5$, $5 - 2 = ?$	(Version with "more"): Julie has three more apples than Lucy. Lucy has two apples. How many apples does Julie have? (Version with "fewer"): Lucy has 3 fewer apples than Julie. Lucy has two apples. How many apples does Julie have? $2 + 3 = ?$, $3 + 2 = ?$	(Version with "more"): Julie has three more apples than Lucy. Julie has five apples. How many apples does Lucy have? (Version with "fewer"): Lucy has 3 fewer apples than Julie. Julie has five apples. How many apples does Lucy have? $5 - 3 = ?$, $? + 3 = 5$

[1]These take apart situations can be used to show all the decompositions of a given number. The associated equations, which have the total on the left of the equal sign, help children understand that the = sign does not always mean makes or results in but always does mean is the same number as.

[2]Either addend can be unknown, so there are three variations of these problem situations. Both Addends Unknown is a productive extension of this basic situation, especially for small numbers less than or equal to 10.

[3]For the Bigger Unknown or Smaller Unknown situations, one version directs the correct operation (the version using more for the bigger unknown and using less for the smaller unknown). The other versions are more difficult.

[6]Adapted from Box 2-4 of Mathematics Learning in Early Childhood, National Research Council (2009, pp. 32, 33).

TABLE 2. Common multiplication and division situations.[7]

	Unknown Product $3 \times 6 = ?$	Group Size Unknown ("How many in each group?" Division) $3 \times ? = 18$, and $18 \div 3 = ?$	Number of Groups Unknown ("How many groups?" Division) $? \times 6 = 18$, and $18 \div 6 = ?$
Equal Groups	There are 3 bags with 6 plums in each bag. How many plums are there in all? *Measurement example.* You need 3 lengths of string, each 6 inches long. How much string will you need altogether?	If 18 plums are shared equally into 3 bags, then how many plums will be in each bag? *Measurement example.* You have 18 inches of string, which you will cut into 3 equal pieces. How long will each piece of string be?	If 18 plums are to be packed 6 to a bag, then how many bags are needed? *Measurement example.* You have 18 inches of string, which you will cut into pieces that are 6 inches long. How many pieces of string will you have?
Arrays,[4] Area[5]	There are 3 rows of apples with 6 apples in each row. How many apples are there? *Area example.* What is the area of a 3 cm by 6 cm rectangle?	If 18 apples are arranged into 3 equal rows, how many apples will be in each row? *Area example.* A rectangle has area 18 square centimeters. If one side is 3 cm long, how long is a side next to it?	If 18 apples are arranged into equal rows of 6 apples, how many rows will there be? *Area example.* A rectangle has area 18 square centimeters. If one side is 6 cm long, how long is a side next to it?
Compare	A blue hat costs $6. A red hat costs 3 times as much as the blue hat. How much does the red hat cost? *Measurement example.* A rubber band is 6 cm long. How long will the rubber band be when it is stretched to be 3 times as long?	A red hat costs $18 and that is 3 times as much as a blue hat costs. How much does a blue hat cost? *Measurement example.* A rubber band is stretched to be 18 cm long and that is 3 times as long as it was at first. How long was the rubber band at first?	A red hat costs $18 and a blue hat costs $6. How many times as much does the red hat cost as the blue hat? *Measurement example.* A rubber band was 6 cm long at first. Now it is stretched to be 18 cm long. How many times as long is the rubber band now as it was at first?
General	$a \times b = ?$	$a \times ? = p$, and $p \div a = ?$	$? \times b = p$, and $p \div b = ?$

[4]The language in the array examples shows the easiest form of array problems. A harder form is to use the terms rows and columns: The apples in the grocery window are in 3 rows and 6 columns. How many apples are in there? Both forms are valuable.
[5]Area involves arrays of squares that have been pushed together so that there are no gaps or overlaps, so array problems include these especially important measurement situations.

[7]The first examples in each cell are examples of discrete things. These are easier for students and should be given before the measurement examples.

TABLE 3. The properties of operations. Here a, b and c stand for arbitrary numbers in a given number system. The properties of operations apply to the rational number system, the real number system, and the complex number system.

Associative property of addition	$(a + b) + c = a + (b + c)$
Commutative property of addition	$a + b = b + a$
Additive identity property of 0	$a + 0 = 0 + a = a$
Existence of additive inverses	For every a there exists $-a$ so that $a + (-a) = (-a) + a = 0$.
Associative property of multiplication	$(a \times b) \times c = a \times (b \times c)$
Commutative property of multiplication	$a \times b = b \times a$
Multiplicative identity property of 1	$a \times 1 = 1 \times a = a$
Existence of multiplicative inverses	For every $a \neq 0$ there exists $1/a$ so that $a \times 1/a = 1/a \times a = 1$.
Distributive property of multiplication over addition	$a \times (b + c) = a \times b + a \times c$

TABLE 4. The properties of equality. Here a, b and c stand for arbitrary numbers in the rational, real, or complex number systems.

Reflexive property of equality	$a = a$
Symmetric property of equality	If $a = b$, then $b = a$.
Transitive property of equality	If $a = b$ and $b = c$, then $a = c$.
Addition property of equality	If $a = b$, then $a + c = b + c$.
Subtraction property of equality	If $a = b$, then $a - c = b - c$.
Multiplication property of equality	If $a = b$, then $a \times c = b \times c$.
Division property of equality	If $a = b$ and $c \neq 0$, then $a \div c = b \div c$.
Substitution property of equality	If $a = b$, then b may be substituted for a in any expression containing a.

TABLE 5. The properties of inequality. Here a, b and c stand for arbitrary numbers in the rational or real number systems.

Exactly one of the following is true: $a < b$, $a = b$, $a > b$.
If $a > b$ and $b > c$ then $a > c$.
If $a > b$, then $b < a$.
If $a > b$, then $-a < -b$.
If $a > b$, then $a \pm c > b \pm c$.
If $a > b$ and $c > 0$, then $a \times c > b \times c$.
If $a > b$ and $c < 0$, then $a \times c < b \times c$.
If $a > b$ and $c > 0$, then $a \div c > b \div c$.
If $a > b$ and $c < 0$, then $a \div c < b \div c$.

Notes

Notes

Notes